A PHILOSOPHER LOOKS AT SCIENCE

A PHILOSOPHER
LOOKS AT SCIENCE

ALFRED NORTH WHITEHEAD

Philosophical Library
New York

Thanks are due to the following copyright holders for permission to use their material:

Journal of the Association of Teachers of Mathematics for the Southeastern Part of England. "Mathematics and Liberal Education," Volume I, Number 1 (1912).

Universities Bureau of the British Empire. "Science in General Education," from Proceedings of the Second Congress of the Universities of the Empire, 1921.

Oxford University Press. "The First Physical Synthesis," from F. S. Marvin: "Science and Civilization."

Encyclopedia Britannica. "Axioms of Geometry," "Mathematics," from 11th issue.

The Times Publishing Company, Limited. "Einstein's Theory," from *The Times Educational Supplement,* February 12, 1920.

Library of Living Philosophers. Paul Arthur Schilpp, Editor. "Mathematics and the Good," from Volume III, *The Library of Living Philosophers,* Northwestern University Press; permission granted by the editor and publishers of *The Library of Living Philosophers.*

PUBLISHER'S NOTE

Alfred North Whitehead enjoyed one of the most distinguished and fruitful careers in contemporary philosophy. Born in Great Britain in 1861, he trained in mathematics and philosophy at Cambridge and later taught there. After further teaching assignments at University College in London and at the Imperial College of Science and Technology, he removed in 1924 to the United States to become Professor of Philosophy at Harvard, a post he held until his retirement in 1938.

Whitehead's career may be roughly divided into three periods. The first culminated in 1913 with publication of the last volume of *Principia Mathematica,* which he authored with Bertrand Russell and which served as the literary basis for the founding of modern mathematical logic. His second period, in which he was mainly concerned with developing a philosophy of natural science, began generally with his *An Enquiry Concerning the Principles of Natural Knowledge* (1919) and terminated in *Science and the Modern World* (1925), which already mentioned but not yet attempted a metaphysical synthesis of existence. His third period brought him directly into the area of speculative philosophy and metaphysics, and his views on being and existence are most concretely reflected in *Process and Reality* (1929) and *Modes of Thought* (1938).

The present book is a collection of Whitehead's essays written over the span of his long career. In a sense, the title is redundant, since, as well as being a philosopher, the author was also a scientist. However, through these essays runs the thread of Whitehead's philosophical point of view, and he deals with science not in the scientific abstract, but in its applications to the human order.

CONTENTS

Mathematics and the Good

ABOUT TWO THOUSAND three hundred years ago a famous lecture was delivered. The audience was distinguished: among others it included Aristotle and Xenophon. The topic of the lecture was The Notion of The Good. The lecturer was competent: he was Plato.

The lecture was a failure, so far as concerned the elucidation of its professed topic; for the lecturer mainly devoted himself to Mathematics. Since Plato with his immediate circle of disciples, the Notion of The Good has disengaged itself from mathematics. Also in modern times eminent Platonic scholars with a few exceptions successfully conceal their interest in mathematics. Plato, throughout his life, maintained his sense of the importance of mathematical thought in relation to the search for the ideal. In one of his latest writings he terms such ignorance "swinish." That is how he would characterize the bulk of Platonic scholars of the last century. The epithet is his, not mine.

But undoubtedly his lecture was a failure; for he did not succeed in making evident to future generations his intuition of mathematics as elucidating the notion of The Good. Many mathematicians have been good men—for example, Pascal and Newton. Also many philosophers have been mathematicians. But the peculiar associations of mathematics and The Good remains an undeveloped topic, since its first introduction by Plato. There have been researches into the topic conceived as an interesting characteristic of Plato's mind. But the doctrine, conceived as a basic truth of philosophy, faded from active thought after the first immediate Platonic epoch. Throughout the various ages of European civilization, moral philosophy and mathematics have been assigned to separate departments of university life.

It is the purpose of the present essay to investigate this topic in the light of our modern knowledge. The progress of thought and the expansion of language now make comparatively easy some slight elucidation of ideas which Plato could only express with obscure sentences and misleading myths. You will understand, however, that I am not writing on Plato. My topic is the connection between modern mathematics and the notion of The Good. No reference to any detailed mathematical theorems will be essentially involved. We shall be considering the general nature of the science which is now in process of development. This is a philosophic investigation. Many mathematicians know their details but are ignorant of any philosophic characterization of their science.

II

Within the period of sixty or seventy years preceding the present time, the progressive civilization of the European races has undergone one of the most profound changes in human history. The whole world has been affected; but the origination of the revolution is seated in the races of western Europe and Northern America. It is a change of point of view. Scientific thought had developed with a uniform trend for four centuries, namely, throughout the sixteenth, seventeenth, eighteenth, and nineteenth centuries. In the seventeenth century, Galileo, Descartes, Newton, and Leibniz elaborated the set of concepts, mathematical and physical, within which the whole movement was confined. The culmination may be placed in the decade from 1870 to 1880. At that time Helmholtz, Pasteur, Darwin, and Clerk-Maxwell were developing their discoveries. It was a triumph which produced the death of the period. The change affects every department of thought. In this chapter I emphasize chiefly the shift in the scope of mathematical knowledge. Many of the discoveries which were effective in producing this revolution were made a century earlier than the decade which is here chosen as the final culmination. But the wide realization of their joint effect took place in the fifty years subsequent to 1880. May I add, as an aside, that in addition to its main topic of mathematics and The Good, this chapter is also designed to illustrate how thought develops from epoch to epoch, with its slow half-disclosures? Apart from such knowledge you cannot understand either Plato, or any other philosopher.

III

In order to understand the change, let us conceive the development of an intellectual life which initiated its growth about the year 1870, at the age of about nine or ten years. The whole story reads like a modern version of a Platonic dialogue—for example, the *Theaetetus* or the *Parmenides*. At the commencement of his intellectual life the child would have known the multiplication table up to twelve-times-twelve. Addition, subtraction, multiplication, and division had been mastered. Simple fractions were familiar notions. The decimal notation for fractions was added in the next two or three years. In this way, the whole basis of arithmetic was soon mastered by the young pupil.

In the same period Geometry and Algebra were introduced. In Geometry, the notions of points, lines, planes, and other surfaces are fundamental. The procedure is to introduce some complex pattern of these entities defined by certain relationships between its parts and then to investigate what other relationships in that pattern are implicitly involved in these assumptions. For example, a right-angled triangle is introduced. It is then proved that—assuming Euclidean Geometry—the square on the hypotenuse is equal to the sum of the squares on the other sides.

This example is interesting. For a child can easily look on a figure of a right-angled triangle—as drawn on the black-board by his teacher—without the notion of the squares on the various sides arising in his consciousness. In other words, a defined pattern—such as a right-angled triangle—does not disclose its various intricacies to immediate consciousness.

This curious limitation of conscious understanding is the fundamental fact of epistemology. The child knew what his teacher was talking about, namely, the right-angled triangle quite evidently suggested on the board by the thick chalk lines. And yet the child did not know the infinitude of properties which were implicitly involved.

The primary factors in the boy's concept of a right-angled triangle—as he looked at the black-board—were points, lines, straightness of lines, angles, right-angles. No one of these notions has any meaning apart from the reference to the all-enveloping space. A point has definite position in space, but does not (as then explained) share in any spatial extension. Lines and straight lines have position and also do share in spatial relations between straight lines. Thus no one of the notions involved in the concept of a right-angled triangle has any meaning apart from reference to the spatial system involved.

IV

At that date, apart from a small selection even among eminent mathematicians, it was presupposed that there was only one coherent analysis of the notion of space; in other words, that any two people talking about space must refer to the same system of relations, provided that you expressed a full analysis of every ramification of their meanings. The aim of mathematics, according to their belief, and according to Plato's belief, and according to Euclid's belief, was the adequate expression of this unique, coherent notion of spatiality. We now know that this notion, which had triumphed for about two thousand four hundred years as the necessary foundation for any physical science, was a mistake. It was a glorious mistake: for apart from the simplification thus introduced into the foundations of thought, our modern physical science would have had no agreed simplification of presuppositions by means of which it could express itself.

Thus, the error promoted the advance of learning up to the close of the nineteenth century. At the close of that period, it obstructed the proper expression of scientific ideas. Luckily the mathematicians—at least some of them—had got ahead of the sober thoughts of sensible men of science, and had invented all sorts of fantastic variations from orthodox geometry. At the turn of the centuries, that is, between 1890 and 1910, it was discovered that these variant types of geometry were of essential importance for the expression of our modern scientific knowledge.

From the faint beginnings of geometry, in Egypt and Mesopotamia, up to the present is a stretch of time extending for almost four thousand years. Throughout the whole period this error of a unique geometry has prevailed. Our notions of to-day have a history of about one hundred to a hundred and fifty years. We enjoy the pleasurable satisfaction that "Now we know."

We shall never understand the history of exact scientific knowledge unless we examine the relation of this feeling "Now we know" to the types of learning prevalent in each epoch. In some shape or other it is always present among the dominant group who are preserving and promoting civilized learning. It is a misapplication of that sense of success which is essential for the maintenance of any enterprise. Can this misapplication be characterized? We may complete the phrase "Now we know" by an adverb. We can mean "Now we know— *in part*"; or we can mean "Now we know—*completely*." The distinction between the two phrases marks the difference between Plato and Aristotle, so far as their influence on future generations is concerned. The notion of the complete self-sufficiency of any item of finite knowledge is the fundamental error of dogmatism. Every such item derives its truth, and its very meaning, from its unanalysed relevance to the background which is the unbounded Universe. Not even the simplest notion of arithmetic escapes this inescapable condition for existence. Every scrap of our knowledge derives its meaning from the fact that we are factors in the universe, and are dependent on the universe for every detail of our experience. The thorough sceptic is a dogmatist. He enjoys the delusion of complete futility. Wherever there is the sense of self-sufficient completion, there is the germ of vicious dogmatism. There is no entity which enjoys an isolated self-sufficiency of existence. In other words, finitude is not self-supporting.

The summarized conclusion of this discussion is that geometry, as studied through the ages, is one chapter of the doctrine of Pattern; and that Pattern as known to finite discrimination, is a partial disclosure with an essential relevance to the background of the Universe. Also the term "Geometry" refers to a genus of patterns; and this genus includes a variety of species.

v

We now turn to the discussion of Number, considered as a fundamental mathematical notion. This section can be shortened, because many relevant deflections have already been expressed in the previous examination of Geometry.

The doctrine of number from the Greek period onwards has always included queer little contradictions which thoughtful people disregarded. In the last quarter of the nineteenth century, a more thorough examination of the whole subject, initiated by Georg Cantor and Frege in Germany and Austria, and by Peano and Pieri in Italy, and in England by students of symbolic logic, disclosed a number of awkward questions. Finally Bertrand Russell produced a peculiarly glaring self-contradiction in the current reasoning. I well remember that he explained it to Frege in a private letter. Frege's answer commenced with the exclamation, "Alas, arithmetic totters!"

Frege was correct: Arithmetic tottered and still totters. But Bertrand Russell was equal to the occasion. We were then in the midst of writing a book entitled, *Principia Mathematica*. Russell introduced the notion of "types" of entities. According to that doctrine, the notion of number should only be applied to a group of entities of the same type. Thus the number "three" as applied to entities of one type has a different meaning to the number "three" as applied to entities of another type. For example, if we are considering two different types, there are two different meanings of the number "three."

Russell was perfectly correct. By confining numerical reasoning within one type, all the difficulties are avoided. He had discovered a rule of safety. But unfortunately this rule cannot be expressed apart from the presupposition that the notion of number applies beyond the limitations of the rule. For the number "three" in each type, itself belongs to different types. Also each type is itself of a distinct type from other types. Thus, according to the rule, the conception of two different types is nonsense, and the conception of two different meanings of the number three is nonsense. It follows that our only way of understanding the rule is nonsense. It follows that the rule must be limited to the notion of a rule of safety, and that the complete explanation of number awaits an understanding of the relevance of the notion of the varieties of multiplicity to the infinitude of things. Even in arithmetic you cannot get rid of a subconscious reference to the unbounded universe. You are abstracting details from a totality, and are imposing limitations on your abstraction. Remember that a refusal to think does not imply the non-existence of entities for thought. Our conscious thought is an abstraction of entities from the background of existence. Thought is one form of emphasis.

<h2 style="text-align:center">VI</h2>

Finally in this survey of mathematical notions we come to Algebra. Who invented Algebra? It was invented "in Arabia" or "in India," you all want to tell me. In one sense that is true—namely, the useful symbolism for the algebraic ideas started in one or other, or in both, of those countries. But there is a further question, which, I am sure, would have interested Plato if he had known about Algebra. Who invented the fundamental idea which is thus symbolized?

What is the fundamental notion at the base of Algebra? It is the notion of "*Any* example of a given sort, in abstraction from some particular exemplification of the example or of the sort."

VII

The first animal on this Earth, who even for a moment entertained this notion, was the first rational creature. You can observe animals choosing between *this thing* or *that thing*. But animal intelligence requires concrete exemplification. Human intelligence can conceive of a type of things in abstraction from exemplification. The most obvious disclosures of this characteristic of humanity are mathematical concepts and ideals of the Good—ideals which stretch beyond any immediate realization.

Any practical experience of exactness of realization is denied to mankind: Whereas mathematics, and ideals of perfection, are concerned with exactness. It is the difference between practice and theory. All theory demands exact notions, somewhere or other, however concealed. In practice exactness vanishes: the sole problem is, "Does it Work?" But the aim of practice can only be defined by the use of theory; so the question "Does it Work?" is a reference to theory. Also the importance of theory resides in its reference to practice. The vagueness of practice is energized by the clarity of ideal experience.

No one has ever observed in practice any exact mathematical notion. Consider the child as he learnt his geometry. He never observed an exact point or an exact line, or exact straightness, or an exact circle. Such things were unrealized ideals in the child's mind. So much will be conceded by the man of practical good sense. But when we pass to arithmetic he stalls. You can hear him saying—perhaps you are saying it yourselves—"I can see one chair, two chairs, three chairs, four chairs, and five chairs, and I can observe that two chairs and three chairs when assembled together form a group of five chairs." In this way, our sensible friend has observed exactly exemplifications of arithmetical notions and of an arithmetic theorem.

Now the question is—Has he observed exactly, or, Has he had exact notions elicited in his conceptual experience? In what sense did he observe exactly one chair? He observed a vague differentiation of the general context of his visual experience. But suppose we pin him down to one billionth of an inch. Where does the chair end and the rest of things begin? Which atom belongs to the chair, and which atom belongs to surrounding space? The chair is perpetually gaining and losing atoms. It is not exactly differentiated from its surroundings, nor is it exactly self-identical as time slips by. Again, consider the chair during long periods. It gradually changes, even throughout its solid wooden parts. At the end of a million years in a cave, it becomes fragile, and dissolves at a touch. A slow, imperceptible change is always in progress.

Remember that the human concepts of one inch in length, and of one second of time, as being reasonable basic quantities, are purely relevant to human life. Further, the modern discoveries of physicists and astronomers have disclosed to us the relevance of minute, and of immense, happenings. Our exact conceptual experience is a mode of emphasis. It vivifies the ideals which invigorate the real happenings. It adds the perception of worth and beauty to the mere transition of sense-experience. It is by reason of the conceptual stimulus that the sunset displays the glory of the sky. By this statement, it is not meant that a feeble train of explicit thoughts works the miracle. It is the transformation of the real experience into its ideal limit. Our existence is invigorated by conceptual ideals, transforming vague perceptions.

We cannot understand the flux which constitutes our human experience unless we realize that it is raised above the futility of infinitude by various successive types of modes of emphasis which generate the active energy of a finite assemblage. The superstitious awe of infinitude has been the bane of philosophy. The infinite has no properties. All value is the gift of finitude which is the necessary condition for activity. Also activity means the origination of patterns of assemblage, and mathematics is the study of pattern. Here we find the essential clue which relates mathematics to the study of the good, and the study of the bad.

VIII

You will notice that earlier in this essay we have emphasized that there are no self-existent finite entities. The finite essentially refers to an unbounded background. We have now arrived at the converse doctrine, namely, that infinitude in itself is meaningless and valueless. It acquires meaning and value by its embodiment of finite entities. Apart from the finite, the infinite is devoid of meaning and cannot be distinguished from nonentity. The notion of the essential relatedness of all things is the primary step in understanding how finite entities require the unbounded universe, and how the universe acquires meaning and value by reason of its embodiment of the activity of finitude.

Among philosophers, Spinoza emphasized the fundamental infinitude and introduced a subordinate differentiation by finite modes. Also conversely, Leibniz emphasized the necessity of finite monads and based them upon a substratum of Deistic infinitude. Neither of them adequately emphasized the fact that infinitude is mere vacancy apart from its embodiment of finite values, and that finite entities are meaningless apart from their relationship beyond themselves. The notion of "understanding" requires some grasp of how the finitude of the entity in question requires infinity, and also some notion of how infinity requires finitude. This search for such understanding is the definition of philosophy. It is the reason why mathematics, which deals with finite

18

patterns, is related to the notion of the Good and to the notion of the Bad.

The great religions illustrate this doctrine. Buddhism emphasizes the sheer infinity of the divine principle, and thereby its practical influence has been robbed of energetic activity. The followers of the religion have lacked impulse. The doctrinal squabbles of Christianity have been concerned with the characterization of the infinite in terms of finitude. It was impossible to conceive energy in other terms. The very notion of goodness was conceived in terms of active opposition to the powers of evil, and thereby in terms of the limitation of deity. Such limitation was explicitly denied and implicitly accepted.

IX

The history of the science of algebra is the story of the growth of a technique for representation of finite patterns. Algebra is one chapter in the large technique, which is language. But, in the main, language indicates its meanings by means of casual associations as they arise in human history. It is true that language strives to embody some aspects of those meanings in its very structure. A deep sounding word embodies the deep solemnity of grief. In fact, the art of literature, vocal or written, is to adjust the language so that it embodies what it indicates.

But the larger part of what language physically presents is irrelevant to the meaning indicated. The sentence is a sequence of words. But this sequence is, in general, irrelevant to the meaning. For example, "Humpty-Dumpty sat on a wall" involves a sequence which is irrelevant to the meaning. The wall is in no sense subsequent to Humpty-Dumpty. Also the posture of sitting might have been realized simultaneously with the origination of the sitter and the wall. Thus the verbal order has the faintest reference to the idea conveyed. It is true that by exciting expectation, and by delay, the verbal order does work on the emotions of the recipient. But the sort of emotion, thus aroused, depends on the character of the recipient. Algebra reverses the relative importance of the factors in ordinary language. It is essentially a written language, and it endeavours to exemplify in its written structures the patterns which it is its purpose to convey. It may not be always wholly successful in this endeavour. But it does invert the ordinary habits of language. In the usage of Algebra, the pattern of the marks on paper is a particular instance of the pattern to be conveyed to thought.

Also there is an enlargement of the notion of "any." In arithmetic we write "two plus three" equals "three plus two." We are considering two processes of assemblage. The type of assemblage is indicated by the word —or sign—"plus," and its meaning is restricted by the reference to number. The two procedures are asserted to issue in groups with identical number of members. This number is in fact "five"; but it is not mentioned.

Now in algebra, the restriction of thought to particular numbers is avoided. We write "$x + y = y + x$" where x and y are any two numbers. Thus the emphasis on pattern, as distinct from the special entities involved in the pattern, is increased. Thus algebra in its initiation involved an immense advance in the study of pattern. Relationships of diverse patterns, such as that involved in the Binomial Theorem, entered into human thought. Of course, algebra grew slowly. For centuries it was conceived as a mode of asking for the solution of equations. Somewhere in mediæval times, an unfortunate emperor, or other bigwig, together with his court, had to listen to a learned Italian expounding the solution of a cubic equation. Poor men—a lovely Italian afternoon was wasted! They would have yawned if their interest had not been sustained by the sense of magic.

x

At the beginning of the nineteenth century, Algebra was the study of patterns involved in the various ways of assembling numbers, so that each assemblage issued in the indication of one number, conceived as the outcome of that assemblage. The relation of equality between two assemblages meant that both assemblages indicated the same number. But the interest was directed to the two patterns of assemblage, with their identical indications. In this way, certain general characteristics of patterns of number as realized in the evolving universe were identified with characteristics of patterns of marks on two-dimensional surfaces—usually sheets of paper. Such identities of pattern of meaning with pattern of written marks, or sound variation, are a subordinate characteristic of ordinary language, though of some importance in respect to spoken language. But this identity is the major characteristic of algebraic language.

To-day, surveying the first half of the twentieth century, we find an immense extension of algebra. It has been extended beyond the field of number, and applies to a large group of patterns in which number is a subordinate factor. Very often when number is explicitly admitted, its major use is to provide names, as it is employed for the naming of houses. Thus mathematics is now being transformed into the intellectual analysis of types of pattern.

The notion of the importance of pattern is as old as civilization. Every art is founded on the study of pattern. Also the cohesion of social systems depends on the maintenance of patterns of behaviour; and advances in civilization depend on the fortunate modification of such behaviour patterns. Thus the infusion of pattern into natural occurrences, and the stability of such patterns, and the modification of such patterns, is the necessary condition for the realization of the Good.

Mathematics is the most powerful technique for the understanding of pattern, and for the analysis of the relationships of patterns. Here we reach the fundamental justification for the topic of Plato's lecture. Having regard to the immensity of its subject-matter mathematics, even modern mathematics, is a science in its babyhood. If civilization continues to advance, in the next two thousand years the overwhelming novelty in human thought will be the dominance of mathematical understanding.

The essence of this generalized mathematics is the study of the most observable examples of the relevant patterns; and applied mathematics is the transference of this study to other examples of the realization of these patterns.

XI

Pattern is only one factor in our realization of experience, either as immediate value or as stimulus to activity for future value. For example, in a picture, the geometrical pattern may be good, but the relationship of colours may be horrible. Also each individual colour may be poverty-stricken, indeterminate, and feeble. This example elicits the truth that no entity is merely characterized by its individual character, or merely by its relationships. Each entity possesses essentially an individual character, and also is essentially a terminal of relationship, potential or actual. Some of the factors of individual character enter into the relationships, and conversely the relationships enter into the character. In other words, no entity can be considered in abstraction from the universe, and no entity can be divested of its own individuality. The traditional logic overstressed the notion of individual character. The notion of "any" frees us from individual character: but there is no entity which is merely "any." Thus when algebra is applied, factors beyond algebraic thought are relevant to the total situation. Returning to the picture, mere geometry is not the whole tale. Colours are relevant.

In a picture colour (including black and white) may be reduced to a minimum, as in a pen-and-ink sketch. But some differentiation of colour is necessary for the physical presentation of geometrical design. On the other hand, colour may be dominant in some glorious work of art. Again, the drawing may be good, and colour effect may be a failure. The whole topic of Good and Evil arises. And you cannot discuss Good and Evil without some reference to the interweaving of divers patterns of experience. The antecedent situation may demand depth of realization, and a thin pattern may thwart conceptual expectation. There is then the evil of triviality—a sketch in place of a full picture. Again, two patterns eliciting intense experience may thwart each other. There is then the intense evil of active deprivation. This type has three forms: a concept may conflict with a reality, or two realities may conflict, or two concepts may conflict.

There may be other types of evil. But we are concerned with the maladjustment of patterns of experience. The total pattern has inhibited the insistent effect of either of its parts. But this notion is meaningless except as a reference to the background of feeling—namely emotional and analytic experience—within which that total pattern arises. Every abstraction derives its importance from its reference to some background of feeling, which is seeking its unity as one individual complex fact in its immediate present. In itself a pattern is neither good nor bad. But every pattern can only exist in virtue of the doom of realization, actual or conceptual. And this doom consigns the pattern to play its part in an uprush of feeling, which is the awakening of infinitude to finite activity. Such is the nature of existence: it is the acquisition of pattern by feeling, in its emphasis on a finite group of selected particulars which are the entities patterned—for example, the spatial arrangements of colours and sounds. But the particulars concerned are not necessarily purely qualitative. A human being is more than an assortment of colours and sounds. The notion of pattern emphasizes the relativity of existence, namely, how things are connected. But the things thus connected are entities in themselves. Each entity in a pattern enters into other patterns, and retains its own individuality in this variety of existence. The crux of philosophy is to retain the balance between the individuality of existence and the relativity of existence. Also each individual entity in one pattern may be capable of analysis, so as to display itself as the unity of achieved pattern. The point that I am emphasizing is the function of pattern in the production of Good or Evil in the finite unit of feeling which embraces the enjoyment of that pattern. Also the essential characterization of mathematics is the study of pattern in abstraction from the particulars which are patterned.

When Plato in his lecture connected mathematics with the notion of the Good, he was defending—consciously or unconsciously—the traditional ways of thought spread through all races of mankind. The novelty was the method of abstraction which the Greek genius was gradually emphasizing. Mathematics, as studied in his own Academy, was an abstraction of geometrical and numerical characterizations from the concrete facts of Athenian life. Aristotle was dissecting animals, and was analysing political constitutions. He conceived of genera and species. He thus abstracted the logical characters from the full-blooded experience. The new epoch of scientific abstractions was arising.

One danger in the use of this technique is the simple-minded use of Logic, whereby an erroneous proposition is merely discarded. All propositions are erroneous unless they are construed in reference to a background which we experience without any conscious analysis. Every scientific proposition which the great scientists of the mid-nineteenth century entertained, was erroneous in the sense in which it was then construed. Their doctrine of space was wrong: their doctrine of matter was wrong: their doctrines of evidence were wrong. The abiding interest of Plato's Dialogues does not lie in their enunciation of abstract doctrines. They are suffused with the implicit suggestion of the concrete unity of experience, whereby every abstract topic obtains its interest.

Abstraction involves emphasis, and emphasis vivifies experience, for good, or for evil. All characteristics peculiar to actualities are modes of emphasis whereby finitude vivifies the infinite. In this way Creativity involves the production of value-experience, by the inflow

24

from the infinite into the finite, deriving special character from the details and the totality of the finite pattern.

This is the abstraction involved in the creation of any actuality, with its union of finitude with infinity. But consciousness proceeds to a second order of abstraction whereby finite constituents of the actual thing are abstracted from that thing. This procedure is necessary for finite thought, though it weakens the sense of reality. It is the basis of science. The task of philosophy is to reverse this process and thus to exhibit the fusion of analysis with actuality. It follows that Philosophy is not a science.

Mathematics and Liberal Education

AN ADDRESS

THE SUBJECT OF my address to-day is the consideration of the part which the elements of mathematics should play in a liberal education for the generality of boys up to the age of nineteen. The boys I mean are, of course, those who are capable of a liberal education. Wealth can do much, but it cannot give brains, and it cannot give character; nor can it give the intellectual interests which come from the union of brains with character. Accordingly, I exclude the residuum of boys, and am thinking of those only with fair brains and decent interests. Happily for England these constitute the great majority of the ordinary students who pass on to our Universities.

It will help us to understand the nature of our problem if we spend a few minutes in examining the ultimate reason for the existing upheaval in the scholastic world. We are, in fact, in the midst of an educational revolution caused by the dying away of the classical impulse which has dominated European thought since the time of the Rennaissance. I find it a little difficult to explain my meaning exactly. I am not referring to the mere teaching of a little more or a little less of Latin and Greek. What I mean is the loss of that sustained reference to classical literature for the sake of finding in it the expression of our best thoughts on all subjects. The Greek masterpieces of literature remain masterpieces of literature, and the labours of a band of brilliant scholars have reinterpreted them to the modern world. But for all that, the scene presented to our view by the human life of to-day is essentially different to that presented either to the Greeks of two thousand years ago, or even to our grandfathers at the beginning of the nineteenth century.

There are three fundamental changes which make an unbridgeable gap. Science now enters into the very texture of our thoughts; its methods and results colour the imaginations of our poets; they modify the conclusions of philosophers and theologians. Again, mechanical inventions, which are the product of science, by altering the material possibilities of life, have transformed our industrial system, and thus have changed the very structure of Society. Finally, the idea of the World now means to us the whole round world of human affairs, from the revolutions of China to those of Peru. Even to our fathers it merely conveyed the idea of the nations of Europe, and, in particular, of the Mediterranean shores. But this provincial phase of thought is rapidly becoming impossible.

The total result of these changes is that the supreme merit of immediate relevance to the full compass of modern life has been lost to classical literature. To make a trivial example: in Athens, a reference to a potter's wheel might recall vivid memories of habitual sights; in London, it requires a footnote. Whether we regret it or no, the absolute dominance of classical ideas in education is necessarily doomed.

But it is not possible to alter the whole basis of our curriculum by a mere change in the time-table. In the first place, there is the difficulty which amateur reformers in education usually forget—that there is no time. Lack of time is the rock upon which the fairest educational schemes are wrecked. It has wrecked that scheme which our fathers constructed to meet the growing demand for the introduction of modern ideas. They simply increased the number of subjects taught. Latin and Greek were to be retained, the time given to mathematics enlarged, modern history and physical science to be added; and, at the same time, geography, music, draw-

27

ing, and nature studies were not to be neglected. Also, of course, modern languages were regarded as indispensable.

The task of education with such a scheme of studies is frankly impossible. In all modern educational reform the watchword must be "concentration."

But if we examine this older curriculum as it existed in practice, we shall note, unless I am much mistaken, that in general it possessed one very striking peculiarity. It was believed, with some reason, that every cultivated idea had found its best expression in the classical literatures. The result was that the whole of the general training in ideas was annexed, and with some reason, to the study of the classical languages. Other studies were, in fact, pursued as mere technical acquirements. The boys might learn both German and Greek; but it was from Sophocles and not from Goethe that they drew their ideas. Mathematics, for example, was divested of all discussion of ideas, and reduced to the aimless acquirement of formal methods of procedure. In other words, modern thought was not introduced into the educational curriculum, but merely modern technique. If, for the mass of boys and young men, we are to concentrate our education upon modern subjects, we must first transform them into a real vehicle for the inculcation of ideas. We have, in fact, to civilize them.

Now, nothing is more difficult than to transmit to our pupils real general ideas, as distinct from pretentious phrases. Nobody with any sense can confront a class for long without discovering that all sound teaching is concerned with definite, accurate achievements on the part of the pupils—to construe grammatically a Latin sentence, to solve a quadratic equation, or to find, with some precision, the specific heat of lead. Vague generalities are worse than useless, and if we attempt to embody abstractions in short, precise formulæ, the pupils will simply learn them by heart as empty sounds.

In view of this difficulty, let us examine briefly how the classical languages achieved their undoubted success as vehicles of a liberal education. The advantage of education based upon them is that at every step definite aims are placed before the learner. He has to construe the author, to know the meaning and grammatical status of each word, and to render the sense in the precise equivalent English. There is nothing vague in all this; it is an accurate achievement which the pupil has to accomplish. It has also the useful property, which every teacher will appreciate, that it is easy to test whether the pupil has in reality tried to accomplish his task. He may not make sense of his translation, but he can at least know the meaning of the various words and their cases or their tenses; and, in addition to all this, the classical languages possess the supreme merit that great ideas are simultaneously presented to the mind. The noblest authors of Greece and Rome can be read. Some of us may still remember construing in our school-days Lucretius' reflections on the nature of the universe, and the account of the battle of the harbour of Syracuse, its triumph and its despair.

I will not consider further the question of the literary side of education. Not because I undervalue its importance, but because we are especially responsible for the logical training. We have really two general aims before us. In the first place, we have to teach what logic is. I do not mean by this that we should indulge in the somewhat futile task of affixing names to elementary logical processes after the manner of primers in formal logic. But we have to make our pupils feel by an acquired instinct what it means to be logical, and to know a precise idea when they see it; or, rather what unfortunately is more often wanted, to know an unprecise idea when they see it. In the second place, we have to make them understand that logic applies to life. This is, in fact, the harder task. Most people agree that there are abstract precise ideas capable of logical treatment, but very few really believe that a sensible man need take any account of them. Such and such ideas, they will say, are all right in theory, but in practice they are useless. It is here that the astounding success of modern science in transforming the world makes an examination of the elements of its logical methods so vital a part of modern education. In this region ancient thought is frankly useless. It is possible that the Greeks were in all respects abler than we are, and that, if here, they would conduct our scientific investigations in a manner superior to anything to which we can attain. But the ancient Greeks are not here, and the fact remains that our modern scientific thought completely overshadows anything of the same sort which existed in the ancient world. In this connection it is a mistake to think that the Greeks discovered the elements of mathematics, and that we have added the advanced parts of the subject. The opposite is more nearly the case; they were interested in the higher parts of the subject and never discovered its elements. The practical elements, as they are now employed in physical science, and the theoretical elements upon which the whole reposes, were alike unknown to them. Weierstrass' theory of limits and Georg Cantor's theory of sets of points are much more allied to Greek modes of thought than are our modern arithmetic, our modern theory of positive and negative numbers, our modern graphical representation of the functional relation, or our modern idea of the algebraic variable. Elementary mathematics is one of the most characteristic creations of modern thought. It is characteristic of modern thought by virtue of the intimate way in which it correlates theory and practice.

I make this point in no idle spirit, but to enforce a very serious conclusion. In the past, the teaching of elementary mathematics has suffered, not only because its ideas were sucked away from it by the dominant classics, but also because it was treated as a collection of mere uninteresting prolegomena to more advanced parts of the subject. But the mass of pupils never advanced to these further parts, and, in consequence, gained nothing but a set of purposeless dodges.

We must conceive elementary mathematics as a subject complete in itself, to be studied for its own sake. It must be purged of every element which can only be justified by reference to a more prolonged course of study. There can be nothing more destructive of true education than to spend long hours in the acquirement of ideas and methods which lead nowhere. It is fatal to all intellectual vitality. It produces, on the one hand, a sense of incompetence, of lack of grasp, and of inability really to penetrate to the true meaning of things; and, on the other hand, by a natural revolt of the self-respecting intellect, it produces a distaste for ideas, and a suspicion that they are all equally futile. I have had great experience with the average product of our schools as sent up to the Universities. My general conclusion is not that they have been idle at school, or have been taught carelessly. On the contrary, their education has evidently been supervised with a conscientious vigour. But there is a widely-spread sense of boredom with the very idea of learning. I attribute this to the fact that they have been taught too many things merely in the air, things which have no coherence with any train of thought such as would naturally occur to anyone, however intellectual, who has his being in this modern world. The whole apparatus of learning appears to them as nonsense. Of course, any individual schoolmaster is helpless in this matter; he is in the grip of the examination system. It is here that the utility of such associations as the one which celebrates its meeting to-day is apparent. It enables the results of first-hand experience to acquire the authority of a collective demand capable of constraining the nameless Furies who draw up our schedules of examinations.

But to return to elementary mathematics: we conceive it as a group of abstract ideas, and our course is to have a threefold character, namely: (1) the pupil is finally to be left with a precise perception of the nature of the abstractions acquired by constant use of them, illumined by explanations and finally by precise statements; (2) the logical treatment of such ideas is to be exemplified by trains of reasoning which employ them and interconnect them; and (3) the application of these ideas to the course of nature conceived in its widest sense as including human society is to be made familiar.

The subject, as thus broadly sketched out, is limited by the following considerations: there is very little time; only such ideas are to be introduced as are of fundamental importance to all mathematical reasoning, and they are not to be too complicated for the average boy to understand.

Most of these requisites explain themselves, and I need say nothing more about them. It will be seen that the whole spirit of these suggestions is towards a cutting down of the mere quantity of abstract reasoning to be performed, but towards an extension of the time devoted to a consideration of the ideas in themselves especially by the aid of their applications to examples. By examples, I mean important examples. What we want is one hour of the Caliph Omar, to burn up and utterly destroy all the silly mathematical problems which cumber our text-books. I protest against the presentation of mathematics as a silly subject with silly applications.

For example, take the theory of graphs, which, on its theoretical side, should teach the boys the abstract idea of a functional relation between variable quantities. This abstract idea is embodied in a few simple theoretical examples, such as the rectilinear graph of the linear algebraic function of one variable, the parabolic graph of the quadratic function, also the wavy graphs of the sine and cosine illustrate the general nature of periodic functions. In this way the boy grows familiar with the idea of an abstract precise law. If time permits the law of the inverse square can be exhibited in a graph, and also the fundamental law of the geometrical increase by plotting functions such as 2^x, 3^x, etc., and for the abler students by the consideration of the series $\exp\chi$, that is, e^x. But for the mass of boys a few well-chosen examples of precise functional relations would surely be better than a more ambitious course over a wider field.

Now, still keeping for the present to the abstract side of the work, the consideration of the zeros of these functions at once introduces equations as a necessary branch of study. Linear and quadratic equations acquire an important meaning, and so do the zeros of the sine and cosine functions. At this point I suggest the study of abstract algebra might well be stopped. I would utterly sweep away all prolonged multiplications and divisions, and the theories of greatest common measure and least common multiple, and complicated forms of linear and quadratic equations. They lead to nothing important in the boys' minds and consume a vast amount of valuable time. It would be quite sufficient to confine practice in multiplication to cases in which one factor is linear, and practice in division to cases in which the divisor is linear. Similarly, factorization, if admitted, should be rigidly confined to the case of two linear factors with the view of exemplifying the theory of the zeros of quadratic functions. Again, for the mass of boys, the algebraic treatment of fractional expressions consumes valuable time uselessly. Of course, ample practice in algebraic manipulation is necessary, but it should be restricted to a few types of the most necessary operations.

It will be noticed that while advocating the omission of a large part of the algebra usually taught, I would include the definitions of sine and cosine, and the study of their graphs. I do not suggest that trigonometry, properly so called, be introduced. By this I mean the application of the trigonometrical functions to the theory of the triangle. This would, in general, take up far too much time with very little intellectual result. The true use of these functions in elementary mathematics is their representation of the idea of periodicity. Perhaps, however, I am too sanguine in hoping that their comprehension is within the range of the ordinary boy.

The general outcome of these suggestions is that elementary algebra would be restricted to the consideration of the simplest functions of one variable. The golden rule should be that until the end of their course, students should never see expressions with more than one unknown in them. It is traditional at the very commencement of the study of the science to present functions containing a large number of letters, $a, b, c, d, e, f,$ with directions to substitute particular values for them. I am utterly unable to conceive what is the educational value of this inane procedure. All that is wanted to begin with is the calculation of the values of particular cases of the simple functions for particular values of the single variable. Then the idea of any value of the function arises, and, to put the matter technically, we come to the letter "y" standing by itself on the left-hand side of the equation, and the function on the right-hand side.

Finally, we *perhaps* reach the idea of algebraic form and introduce the coefficients as parameters with the letters a, b, c. But except for the sake of algebraic form more than one variable, as an argument to a function, is never wanted in elementary study.

So much for the theoretical side of the subject. I have treated this first because in view of further suggestions on the practical applications, it was necessary to explain in what way time was to be gained, and what are the theoretical ideas to be led up to and to be applied.

But I wish emphatically to guard myself against suggesting that such abstract ideas as variable and functionality are best introduced by the consideration of abstract algebraic functions however simple. On the contrary, a preparatory consideration of concrete examples by graphical methods is surely necessary. There we reach one of the chief causes of the weakness of the traditional mathematical training. It is entirely out of relation to the real exhibition of the mathematical spirit in modern thought, with the result that it remained satisfied with examples which were both silly and unsystematic. Now the effect which we want to produce on our pupils is to generate a capacity to apply ideas to the concrete universe. Thus the examples which we choose form the very backbone of our teaching. The study of algebra should commence with a systematic study of the practical application of mathematical ideas of quantity to some important subject. Now what subject can we choose by which to represent the flux of quantities without the necessary intervention of algebraic technique from the very beginning. Many suggestions might be made, and it is obvious that many subjects in competent hands might be equally good. My suggestion in its crudest, and most aggressive, form is that half of the teaching of modern history should be handed over to the mathematicians. The phrase "handed over" is not quite accurate; for the half which I mean is the half which, although the true foundation of all knowledge of nations, is hardly taught. Our classical colleagues, excellent fellows as they are, have their limitations; and among them is this one, that they are not very fitted by their mental equipment to appreciate quantitative estimates of the forces which are moulding modern society. But without such estimates modern history as it unfolds itself before us is a meaningless tangle.

Now among other peculiarities of the nineteenth century is this one, that by initiating the systematic collection of statistics it has made the quantitative study of social forces possible. There are to our hands statistics of trade both external and internal, statistics of railway traffic, statistics of harvest, of prices, of health of population, of education, of crime, of income-tax returns, of national expenditure, of weather, of prices, of pauperism, and of times of sunrise and sunset throughout the year. The reduction of these to graphs, the careful study of the peculiarities of these graphs, the search for correlations among them, and the study of the public events which corresponded in time to peculiarities in graphical form, would teach more mathematics and more knowledge of modern social forces than all our present methods put together. Our relations with our colonies, with France, with Germany, with the United States, could be traced statistically. Problems could be set for solution by the boys—such as to state verbally the effect of war on the social life of a nation as exhibited by the graphs. Also they can be given the statistics and told to exhibit them in graphical form, and to state the general characteristics of the graphs thus obtained. The notion of rates of increase, embodying the essential ideas of the differential calculus, thus emerges.

Finally, theory and practice could be combined by finding graphs which approximately satisfy the simple functional laws which are being simultaneously studied.

I am quite aware that this suggestion of statistical study may seem fantastic, and perhaps be pronounced impossible. Of course, in a rapid first sketch, one cannot hope to have put all the details of the idea in their right relation to one another. But before the whole suggestion is definitely dismissed, I should like to know exactly why it is impossible and why it is fantastic. The information to be imparted is of the utmost importance for the subsequent conduct of life in self-governing communities; it illustrates important abstract ideas, and the means of study lie easily to hand. Also the course of work would involve simple definite efforts on the part of the students. This method of conducting the elementary study of mathematical analysis appears to me to be eminently practical, and at every stage to carry with it its own justification.

The mathematical treatment of our space-ideas is obviously of the first educational importance. I cannot pretend to be very satisfied with the immediate effects of the abolition of Euclid's Elements as a text-book. A lamentable deficiency in logical rigour has crept in, with entirely bad effects on the scholastic value of the subject. My belief is that the science as an educational instrument has been ruined from the time of Euclid downwards by fallacious views of logical method which seem to be both prevalent and traditional. There is an idea that the logical premises of a subject like geometry are propositions which have some peculiar quality of self-evidence, which is not merely one of degree. In fact, it is implied that there are natural premises which have to be used as such because they are self-evident and incapable of proof.

Probably, when the view is thus crudely stated it would be repudiated by everyone. But I believe it to be true that the usual presentation of geometry as a deductive science, based on axioms which the student is simply told to accept, does, in fact, habitually generate this fallacious notion; thereby, the harm done to a sound conception of the relation of logic to induction is nearly as great as is the good received from the training in the art of reason. The same error crops up in an even more pestilential form when authors on mechanics imply that that science is based on separate verifications of the various laws of motion. Half our difficulties in the elementary teaching of the deductive sciences arise from the tacit unconscious acceptance of this abominable heresy.

I am told that there are some animals whose centres of intelligence, such as they are, are fairly uniformly distributed throughout their bodies, so that, however you cut them in half, both parts are equally sensible. Something like this is the case in any science. The propositions which, for some reason or other, claim our credence, are distributed throughout the whole body of the subject. The function of deductive logic is, by the creation of a coherent logical system, to tie them together, so as to enable us to pool their evidence. But often there is more evidence for the more complex propositions than for the premises. The chief requisite for a premise is not obvious truth, but simplicity. There is no obvious truth about the law of gravitation; but the science of attractions, which is founded on it, is verified all along the line in so far as it is applied to ordinary matter.

Thus, in order to pool our evidence for a body of propositions to the utmost extent, it is desirable that the premises assumed should be as few and simple as possible, and, of course, the more fully they claim our credence the better. But none of these requisites are absolutely necessary on pain of logical fallacy. Our selection of premises is arbitrary, and must be guided by the purpose which we have in view. Now these logical considerations have a profound influence on our conceptions of the true mode in which to present geometry. They lead to the conclusion that the old traditional presentation is wrong.

In the first place it is of great importance that students, before considering any logical proofs, should be made thoroughly familiar with the set of ideas and propositions which are to compose the schedule of the subject. They should note that some propositions appear obvious, and that others are capable of experimental verification by the measurement of accurately drawn diagrams.

In this way, a schedule of important propositions should be thoroughly appreciated. Then a selection of some of the simpler and more obvious propositions should be made and treated as logical premises. They are *our* axioms of geometry, not *the* axioms of geometry; and from them, by the most rigid reasoning, justifying every step as we go along, the remainder of the schedule should be proved.

But I would remind you that there is no logical fallacy in retaining a logically redundant set of premises. We can, if we like, point out to our pupils that some of the assumed propositions can be proved from the others, but there is absolutely no necessity to give the proof if we think it too long or too difficult. What is necessary for education is that the pupil should definitely know what propositions have been assumed, that these axioms should carry with them some strong evidence of truth, and that the reasoning should be rigidly accurate and full. But where assumption is so easy, logical fallacies are unpardonable. Also it may be desirable to retain some propositions in the schedule for experimental consideration which are not ultimately subjected to logical proof. For example, the theory of similarity is the foundation of all maps and plans, and it is highly desirable to appreciate its elementary propositions even if they cannot be proved.

But, as in the case of algebra, the schedule should be rigidly purged of all propositions which might appear to the student to be merely curiosities without any important bearings.

But what are the important bearings of geometrical truths? In a sense, the science is its own justification. It is the framework almost instinctively adopted to state our experiences of the universe. In order to explain why we feel tired, we state the number of miles which we have walked; to explain why it took so many days to plough a field, we state its number of acres. In every attempted explanation of the material facts of life we have recourse to geometrical ideas. Geometry is the queen of physical sciences. Accordingly, in a sense, we might bring any geometrical theorem into the schedule. But our time is limited, and we shall do well to concentrate on a few truths of the widest application and of most immediate importance. Whatever we put into the schedule necessarily excludes something else, and this consideration governs our selection.

The treatment of the whole doctrine of similarity makes almost a small subject in itself. It faces us in the selection of the scales of our graphs and other diagrams. Also it naturally coalesces with the doctrine of arithmetical proportion which in its elements receives a simple algebraic treatment. This, again, finds an application in the proportional variation of the entries in statistical tables, corresponding to variations either of population or of other fundamental aggregates. I should like, at this point, to enter a plea for the inclusion of the parallelogram of forces and the polygon of forces as the fundamental example of the application of geometry to science. But already I have been led into a discourse which, against my original intention, has wandered away into a technical discussion.

We have been considering the place of elementary mathematics in a liberal education. What, in a few words, is the final outcome of our thoughts? It is that the elements of mathematics should be treated as the study of a set of fundamental ideas, the importance of which the student can immediately appreciate: that every proposition and method which cannot pass this test, however important for a more advanced study, should be ruthlessly cut out: that with the time thus gained, the fundamental ideas placed before the pupils can be considerably enlarged so as to include what in essence is the method of co-ordinate geometry, the fundamental idea of the differential calculus in relation to rates of increase, and the geometrical notion of similarity. Also, lastly, it has been insisted that important systematic applications of these ideas to the concrete world should be simultaneously studied—for example, some sets of social or scientific statistics and the use of the polygon of forces in the graphical solution of mechanical problems. Again, this rough summary can be further abbreviated into one essential principle, namely, simplify the details and emphasize the important principles and applications.

The suggestions which I have ventured to put forward have been made with unfeigned diffidence. I am emboldened to speak by the conviction that we have now a golden opportunity for reconstituting our scheme of mathematical education. But such opportunities are dangerous. If mathematical teaching is not now revivified by a breath of reality, we cannot hope that it will survive as an important element in the liberal education of the future.

Science in General Education

WE ARE BECOMING aware that in adjusting a curriculum, it is not sufficient to agree that some specified subject should be taught. We have to ask many questions and to make many experiments before we can determine its best relation to the whole body of educational influences which are to mould the pupil.

In the first place it is necessary to keep before our minds that nine-tenths of the pupil's time is, and must be, occupied in the apprehension of a succession of details—it may be facts of history, it may be the translation of a definite paragraph of Thucydides, it may be the observable effects in some definite physical experiment. You cannot learn Science, *passim;* what you do learn in some definite hour of work is perhaps the effect on the temperature of a given weight of boiling water obtained by dropping into it a given weight of lead at another definite temperature, or some analogous detailed set of facts. It is true that all teaching has its rhetorical moments when attention is directed to æsthetic values or to momentous issues. But practical schoolmasters will tell you that the main structure of successful education is formed out of the accurate accomplishment of a succession of detailed tasks. It is necessary to enforce this point at the very beginning of discussion, and to keep it in mind throughout, because the enthusiasm of reformers so naturally dwells on what we may term "the rhetoric of education."

Our second step in thought must be to envisage the principles which should govern the arrangement of the detailed lessons in the subject. An educational cynic will tell you that it does not make much difference what you teach the pupils: they are bound to forget it all when they leave school; the one important thing is, to get the children into the habit of concentrating their thoughts, of applying their minds to definite tasks, and of doing what they are told. In fact, according to this school of thought, discipline, mental and physical, is the final benefit of education, and the content of the ideas is practically valueless. An exception is made for pupils of unusual ability or of unusual twist of interest. I conceive this summary solution of the educational problem to be based on an entirely false psychology, and to be in disagreement with experience. It depends for its plausibility on the erroneous analogy of the intellectual organism with some kind of mechanical instrument such as a knife, which you first sharpen on a hard stone, and then set to cut a number of different things quite disconnected with the stone and the process of sharpening. The other sources of the theory are the disillusionment of tired teachers, and the trenchant judgments of those who will not give the time to think out a complex question. But as this opinion is not likely to be largely represented among members of the Congress, further contemplation of it is unnecessary. In considering the general principles which are to govern our selection of details, we must remember that we are concerned with general education. Accordingly we must be careful to avoid conceiving science either in quantity or quality as it would be presented to the specialists in that subject. We must not assume ample time or unusual scientific ability. Also in recent years the congestion of subjects in the curriculum, combined with the opposing claims of specialism, has led practically all English Schools and the Board of Education to adopt certain principles regulating the relations between general education and special subjects. Our discussion must take these for granted, if we wish to be practical. Education up to the age of sixteen, or sixteen-and-a-half, is to be dominated by the claims of general education, and extended attention to any special subject is to be limited by the claims of the whole balanced curriculum. In the case of a pupil of any reasonable ability there will be time for some specialism; but the ruling principle is, that where the claims of the two clash, the specialism is to be sacrificed to the general education. But after the age of sixteen, the position is reversed. The pupil is expected to devote the larger proportion of his time to some adequate special subject, such as classics, science, mathematics, or history, and the remaining portion to suitably contrasted subsidiary subjects, such as modern languages for a scientist or a mathematician. In other words, before sixteen the special subject is subsidiary to the general education, and after sixteen the general education is subsidiary to the special subject. Accordingly our discussion divides into two sections, namely, science in general education before the age of sixteen, and after the age of sixteen. The second division may also be taken to cover the University stage. This principle of a preliminary general education has set to educationalists a new problem which has not as yet been adequately worked on in any subject. Indeed it is only just dawning on responsible people in its full urgency. But on its solution depends the success of that modern system of education to which we are now committed.

The problem is this: In all schools, with negligible exceptions, the general education has to be arranged with practical uniformity for the school as a whole. In the first place it is not very certain who among the pupils are the future scientists, who the future classical scholars, or who are the future historians. For the greater number, the desirable differentiation will only gradually disclose itself. Secondly, we may not assume that the majority of boys or girls in secondary schools will remain at school after the age of seventeen, and thus continue any portion of the general education after the first period. Accordingly for both these reasons, the preliminary general training in each subject should form a self-contained course, finding its justification in what it has done for the pupil at its termination. If it is not justified then, it never will be, since at this point, in the vast majority of instances, the formal study of the subject ends.

If we examine the cause of the educational dissatisfaction at the end of the last and at the beginning of this century, we shall find that it centres round the fact that the subjects in the curriculum were taught as incomplete fragments. The children were taught their elementary mathematics exactly as though they were to proceed in later years to take their degrees as high wranglers. Of course most of them collapsed at the first stage; and nobody—least of all the children—knew why they had been taught just that selection of meaningless elaborate preliminaries. Anyhow, as they soon forgot it all, it did not seem much to matter. The same criticism applied to the classics, and to other subjects. Accordingly, every subject in the preliminary training must be so conceived and shaped as yielding, during that period, general aptitudes, general ideas, and knowledge of special facts, which, taken in conjunction, form a body of acquirement essential to educated people. Furthermore it must be shown that the valuable part of that body of acquirement could not be more easily and quickly gained in some other way, by some other combination of subjects.

In considering the framing of a scientific curriculum subject to these conditions, we must beware of the fallacy of the soft option. It is this pitfall which has ruined so many promising schemes of reform. It seems such an easy solution, that, in order to gain time, we should shape a course comprising merely the interesting descriptive facts of the subject and the more important and exciting generalizations. In this way our course is self-contained and can easily be compressed into a reasonable time. It will certainly be a failure, and the reason of the failure illustrates the difficulty or the art of education. In order to explain this, let us recur to the educational cynic whom I introduced at the beginning of this paper; for he really is a formidable critic. He will point out that in a few years your pupil will have forgotten the precise nature of any facts which you teach him, and will almost certainly have muddled your generalizations into incorrect forms. The cynic will ask, What is the use of a vague remembrance of the wrong date for the last glacial epoch, and of a totally erroneous idea of the meaning of "the survival of the fittest"? Furthermore, we may well doubt whether your science, as thus taught, will be really interesting. Interest depends upon background, that is to say, upon the relations of the new element of thought or perception to the pre-existing mental furniture. If your children have not got the right background, even "the survival of the fittest" will fail to enthuse them. The interest of a sweeping generalization is the interest of a broad high road to men who know what travel is; and the pleasure of the road has its roots in the labour of the journey. Again facts are exciting to the imagination in so far as they illuminate some scheme of thought, perhaps only dimly discerned or realized, some day-dreams begotten by old racial experience, or some clear-cut theory exactly comprehended. The complex of both factors of interest satisfies the cravings inherent in that mysterious reaching out of experience from sensation to knowledge, and from blind instinct to thoughtful purpose.

The conclusion is that you can only elicit sustained interest from a process of instruction which sets before the pupils definite tasks which keep their minds at stretch in determining facts, in illustrating these facts by ideas, and in illustrating ideas by their application to complex facts. I am simply enforcing the truism that no reform in education can abolish the necessity for hard work and exact knowledge.

Every subject in the general education must pull its weight in contributing to the building up of the disciplined power of definitely controlled thought. Experience amply proves that no one special traning is adequate for this purpose; the classical scholar cannot necessarily focus mathematical ideas, and the mathematician may be a slovenly thinker outside his science, and neither classic nor mathematician may have acquired the habits of procedure requisite for observation and analysis of natural phenomena. In this connection the function of the study of a subject is not so much to produce knowledge as to form habits. It is its business to transmute thought into an instinct which does not smother thought but directs it, to generate the feeling for the important sort of scientific ideas and for the important ways of scientific analysis, to implant the habit of seeking for causes and of classifying by similarities. Equally important is the habit of definitely controlled observation. It is the besetting fallacy of over-intellectual people to assume that education consists in training people in the abstract power of thought. What is important is the welding of thought to observation. The first effect of the union of thought and observation is to make observation exact. You cannot make an exact determination of the passing phenomena of experience unless you have predetermined what it is you are going to observe, so as to fix attention on just those elements of the perceptual field. It is this habit of predetermined perception and the instinctive recognition of its importance which is one of the greatest gifts of science to general education. It is here that practical work in the laboratory, or field work in noting geological or botanical characteristics, is so important. Such work must be made interesting to obtain the proper engrossment of attention, and it must be linked with general ideas and with adequate theory to train in the habit of pre-determining observation by thought. Every training impresses on its recipient a certain character; and the various elements in the general education must be so handled as to enrich the final character of the pupil by their contribution. We have been discussing the peculiar value of science in this respect. It should elicit the habit of first-hand observation, and should train the pupil to relate general ideas to immediate perceptions, and thereby obtain exactness of observation and fruitfulness of thought. I repeat that primarily this acquirement is not an access of knowledge but a modification of character by the impress of habit. Literary people have a way of relegating science to the category of useful knowledge, and of conceiving the impress on character as gained from literature alone. Accordingly I have emphasized this point.

We have, however, not yet exhausted the analysis of the impress on character due to science. The imagination is disciplined and strengthened. The process of thinking ahead of the phenomena is essentially a work of the imagination. Of course it involves only one specific type of imaginative functioning which is thus strengthened, just as poetic literature strengthens another specific type. Undoubtedly there will be some interplay between the types, but we must not conceive the imagination as a definite faculty which is strengthened as a whole by any particular imaginative act of a specific type. Accordingly science should give something to the imagination which cannot be otherwise obtained. If we are finally to sum up in one phrase the peculiar impress on character to be obtained from a scientific training, I would say that it is a certain type of instinctive direction in thought and observation of nature, and a facility of imagination in respect to the objects thus contemplated, issuing in a stimulus towards creativeness. We now turn to the other aspect of science. It is the systematization of supremely useful knowledge. In the modern world men and women must possess a necessary minimum of this knowledge, in an explicit form, and beyond this, their minds must be so trained that they can increase this knowledge as occasion demands. Accordingly the general education during the "pre-sixteen" period must include some descriptive summaries of physiological, botanical, physical, chemical, astronomical, and geological facts, even although it is not possible to choose all those sciences as subjects for serious study in the school curriculum. Especially this is important in the case of physiology owing to the accidental circumstance that we all have bodies.

We see therefore that the scientific curriculum must have a soft element and a hard element. The hard element will consist in the attainment of exact knowledge based on first-hand observation. The laboratory work will be so framed as to illustrate such concepts and theoretical generalizations as the pupil is to know. I would insist that science in this stage of education loses nearly all its value, if its concepts and generalizations are not illustrated and tested by practical work. This union of acquirement of concepts, of comprehension of general laws, of reasoning from them, and of testing by experiment will go slowly at first, because the child's powers of mind have to be built up. The pupil has not got the requisite generalizing faculty ready made, and it is the very purpose of the education to give it to him. Furthermore little bits of diverse sciences are useless for the purpose; with such excessive dispersion the systematic character of science is lost, nor does the knowledge go deep enough to be interesting. We must beware of presenting science as a set of pretentious names for obvious facts or as a set of verbal phrases. Accordingly the hard element in the scientific training should be confined to one or at most two sciences, for example, physics and chemistry. These sciences have also the advantage of being key sciences without which it is hardly possible to understand the others. By the age of sixteen every pupil should have done some hard work at these two sciences, and—generally speaking—it is scarcely possible that there will have been any time for analogous work in any other natural science, after the necessary mathematical time has been allotted. Probably in a four years' course the best quantitative division would be two years of physics and two years of chemistry, and mathematics all the time. But assuredly it is not desirable to do all the physics in the first period of two years, and all the chemistry in the second period. The first simple ideas clustering round the most elementary experiments will undoubtedly be physical and mechanical. But as some serious progress is made the two sciences illustrate each other, and also relieve each other by the width of interest thus developed. For example, the influence of physical conditions, such as temperature, on the rate, and even the possibility, of chemical transformations is an elementary lesson on the unity of nature more valuable than abstract formulation of statement on the subject.

Two factors should go to form the soft element in scientific education. The first and most important is browsing, with the very slightest external direction, and mainly dependent on the wayward impulses of a student's inward springs of interest. No scheme for education, and least of all for scientific education, can be complete without some facility and encouragement for browsing. The dangers of our modern efficient schemes remind one of Matthew Arnold's line[1] "For rigorous teachers seized my youth." Poor youth! Unless we are careful, we shall organize genius out of existence; and some measure of genius is the rightful inheritance of every man. Such browsing will normally take the form either of chemical experiments, or of field work in geology, or in zoology, or in botany, or of astronomical observation with a small telescope. Anyhow, if he can be got to do so, encourage the child to do something for himself according to his own fancy. Such work will reflect back interest on to the hard part of his training. Here the collector's instinct is the ally of science, as well as of art. Also it is surprising how many people—Shelley, for example—whose main interests are literary derive the keenest pleasure from divagations into some scientific pursuit. In his youth, the born poet often wavers between science and literature; and his choice is determined by the chance attraction of one or other of the alternative modes of expressing his imaginative joy in nature. It is essential to keep in mind, that science and poetry have the same root in human nature. Forgetfulness of this fact will ruin, and is ruining, our educational system. Efficient gentlemen are sitting on boards determining how best to adapt the curriculum to a uniform examination. Let them beware lest, proving themselves descendants of Wordsworth's bad man, they

[1] Stanzas from the *Grande Chartreuse*.

> "Take the radiance from the clouds
> In which the sun his setting shrouds."

The other factor should consist of descriptive lectures, designed for the purpose of giving necessary scientific information on subjects such as physiology, and also for the purpose of exciting general interest in the various sciences. No great amount of time need be taken up in this way. I am thinking of about three to six lectures a term. It should be possible to convey some arresting information about most sciences in this way, and in addition to concentrate on the necessary information on particular points which it is desired to emphasize. The difficulty about such lectures is that comparatively few people are able to give them successfully. It requires a peculiar knack. For this reason I suggest that there should be an exchange of lecturers between schools, and also that successful extension lecturers should be asked to take up this kind of work. It is evident that with a little organization and co-operation the thing could be done, though some care would be required in the arrangement of details. Finally we come to the position of science in general education after the age of sixteen. The pupil is now rapidly maturing and the problem assumes entirely a new aspect. We must remember that he is now engaged mainly in studying a special subject such as classics, or history, which he will continue during his subsequent University course. Among other things, his power of abstract thought is growing, and he is taking a keen delight in generalizations. I am thinking of boys in the sixth form and of undergraduates. I suggest that in general practical work should be dropped, so far as any official enforcement is concerned. What the pupil now wants is a series of lectures on some general aspects of sciences, for example, on the conservation of energy, on the theory of evolution and controversies connected with it, such as the inheritance of acquired characters, on the electromagnetic theory of matter and the constitutions of the molecule, and other analogous topics. Furthermore, the applications of science should not be neglected—machinery and its connection with the economic revolution at the beginning of the nineteenth century, the importance of nitrates and their artificial production, coal-tar, aeronautics, and other topics. As in the case of lectures at the earlier stage, not much time should be occupied by them, and also there is the same difficulty in finding the lecturers. I believe that these lectures are easier to give than the more elementary ones. But I think that it will still be found necessary to create some organization so that local talent can be supplemented by external aid.

Also at this stage books can be brought in to help; for example, Marett's *Anthropology* and Myres' *Dawn of History,* both in "The Home University Library," will form a bridge conducting the historians from the general theory of zoological evolution to the classical history which forms the commencement of their own special studies. I merely give this instance to show the sort of thing, and the scale of treatment, that I am thinking about. But this general treatment of science in the later stage of education will lose most of its value, if there is no sound basis laid in the education before the age of sixteen.

I will conclude with a general caution which summarizes the guiding principle of the preceding remarks: There is very little time, and so in the formal teaching above all things we must avoid both an aimless aggregation of details either in class or in laboratory and the enunciation of verbal statements which bring no concrete ideas to the minds of the pupils.

The First Physical Synthesis

THERE ARE IN THE history of civilization certain dates
which stand out as marking either the boundaries or
the culminations of critical epochs. It is true that no
epoch either commences, ends, or sums itself up in one
definite moment. It is brought upon the stage of reality
in the arms of its predecessors, and only yields to its
successor by reason of a slow process of transformation.
Its terminals are conventional. Wherever you choose to
fix them, you can be confronted with good reasons for
an extension or contraction of your period. But the
meridian culmination is sometimes unmistakable, and
it is often marked by some striking events which lend
an almost mystic symbolism to their exact date. Such a
date is the year 1642 of our epoch, the year in which
occurred the death of Galileo and the birth of Newton.
This date marks the centre of that period of about 100
years during which the scientific intellect of Europe was
framing that First Physical Synthesis which has remained
down to our own times as the basis of science. The development of modern Europe from the world of the
Renaissance and the Reformation is unintelligible in its
unique importance without an understanding of the
achievements of these two men. The great civilizations of
Asia and of the classical times in the Mediterranean had
their epochs of artistic and literary triumph, of religious

reformation, and of active scientific speculation. But it was the fortune of modern Europe that during the seventeenth century, amid a ferment of scientific specu- lation, two men, one after the other, appeared, each with a supreme gift of physical intuition, with magnifi- cent powers of abstract generalization, and each with subsidiary endowments exactly suited to the immediate circumstances of the scientific problem, this one a su- preme experimentalist and enough of a mathematician, and that one a supreme mathematician and enough of an experimentalist. Archimedes left no successor. But our modern civilization is due to the fact that in the year when Galileo died, Newton was born. Think for a moment of the possible course of history supposing that the life's work of these two men were absent. At the commencement of the eighteenth century many curi- ous and baffling facts of physical science would have been observed, vaguely connected by detached and ob- scure hypotheses. But in the absence of a clear physical synthesis, with its overwhelming success in the solution of problems which from the most remote antiquity had excited attention, the motive for the next advance would have been absent. All epochs pass, and the scientific ferment of the seventeenth century would have died down. Locke's philosophy would never have been writ- ten; and Voltaire when he visited England would have carried back to France merely a story of expanding com- merce and of the political rivalries between aristocratic factions. Europe might then have lacked the French in- tellectual movement. But the Fates do not always offer the same gifts twice, and it is possible that the eight- eenth century might then have prepared for the western races an intellectual sleep of a thousand years, prosper- ous with the quiet slow exploitation of the American continent, as manual labour slowly subdued its rivers, its forests, and its prairies. I am not concerned to deny that the result might have been happier, for the chariot of Phœbus is a dangerous vehicle. My only immediate thesis is that it would have been very different.

The forms of the great works by which the minds of

Galileo and Newton are best known to us bear plain evidence of the contrast between their situations. In his book entitled, *The Two Systems of the World in Four Dialogues,* and published in 1632, Galileo is arguing with the past; whilst in his *Mathematical Principles of Natural Philosophy,* published in 1687, Newton ignores old adversaries and discussions, and, looking wholly to the future, calmly enunciates definitions, principles, and proofs which have ever since formed the basis of physical science. Galileo represents the assault and Newton the victory. There can be no doubt but that Galileo is the better reading. It is a real flesh and blood document of human nature which has wedged itself between the two austere epochs of Aristotelian Logic and Applied Mathematics. It was paid for also in the heart's blood of the author.

The catastrophe happened in this way: most unfortunately His Holiness, the reigning pope, in an entirely friendly interview after the Inquisition had forbidden the expression of Copernican opinions, made use of the irrefutable argument that, God being omnipotent, it was as easy for him to send the sun and the planets round the earth as to send the earth and the planets round the sun. How unfortunate it is that even an infallible pontiff and the greatest of men of science, with the most earnest desire to understand each other, cannot rid themselves of their presuppositions. The pope was trembling on the verge of the enunciation of the relativity of motion and of space, and in his Dialogues there are passages in which Galileo plainly expresses that same doctrine. But neither of them was sufficiently aware of the full emphasis to be laid upon that truth. Accordingly the next precious ten minutes of the conversation in which Galileo might have cleared away the little misunderstanding were wasted, and as a result there ensued for the world's edification the persecution of Galileo and a clear illustration of the limits of infallibility. The true moral of the incident is the importance of great men keeping their tempers. Galileo was annoyed—and very naturally so, for it was an irritating sort of argument with which to counter a great and saving formulation of scientific ideas. Unfortunately he went away and put the pope's argument into the mouth of Simplicius, the man in the Dialogues who always advances the foolish objections. It is welcomed in the following speech by the leading inter-locutor, Salviatus—I give it in the seventeenth-century translation of Thomas Salusbury:

> "This of yours is admirable, and truly angelical doctrine, to which very exactly that other accords in like manner divine, which whilst it giveth us leave to dispute, touching the constitution of the world, addeth withall (perhaps to the end that the exercise of the minds of men might neither be discouraged nor made bold) that we cannot find out the works made by his hands. Let therefore the Disquisition per-mitted and ordained us by God, assist us in the know-ing, and so much more admiring his greatness, by how much less we find ourselves too dull to penetrate the profound abysses of his infinite wisdom."

At this point the Dialogues end. Galileo always pro-tested that he had meant no discourtesy. But the pope, even if his infallibility tottered, was here assisted by the gift of prophecy and smelt Voltaire. Anyhow in his turn he lost his temper and afterwards remained the bitter enemy of Galileo.

Galileo's supreme experimental genius is shown by the way in which every hint which reached him is turned to account and immediately made to be of importance. He hears of the telescope as a curiosity discovered by a Dutch optician. It might have remained a toy, but in his hands it created a revolution. He at once thought out the principles on which it was based, improved upon its design so as to obviate the inversion of objects, and immediately applied it to a systematic survey of the heavens. The results were startling. It was not a few details that were altered, but an almost sacred sentiment which fell before it. I have often thought that the calmness with which the Church accepted Copernicus and its savage hostility to Galileo can only be accounted for by measuring the ravages made by the telescope on the sacred doctrine of the heavens. It was then seen too late that the Copernican doctrine was the key to the position. But Galileo's Dialogues plainly show that it was not the movement of the earth but the glory of the heavens which was the point at issue. It must be remembered that the heaven, which Christ had taught is within us, was by the popular sentiment of mediæval times placed above us. Accordingly when the telescope revealed the moon and other planets reduced to the measure of the earth, and the sun with evanescent spots, the shock to sentiment was profound. It is the characteristic of shocked sentiment in the case of men whose learning surpasses their genius that they begin to quote Aristotle. Accordingly Aristotle was hurled at Galileo.

The Dialogues are the records of the contemporary dispute between Galileo and the current Aristotelian tradition, and the end of the discussion was the creation of the modern scientific outlook of which Galileo was the first perfect representative—somewhat choleric but entirely whole-hearted.

So far we have been endeavouring to appreciate the climate of opinions amid which Galileo's life was passed —and you will remember that no climate is composed of a succession of uniform days, especially in its springtime. A judicious selection could affix almost any label to the thought of the seventeenth century. What we have to keep in our minds is that at its beginning, so far as science was concerned, men knew hardly more than Aristotle and less than Archimedes, while at its end the main positions of modern science were firmly established.

I will now endeavour to explain the main revolutionary ideas which Galileo impressed upon his contemporaries. The first one was the doctrine of the uniformity of the material universe. This doctrine is now so obvious to us that we can only think of it in the attenuated form of discussions on miracles or on the relations of mind and matter. But in Galileo's time the denial of uniformity went much deeper than that. The different regions of Nature were supposed to function in entirely different ways. This presupposition led to a style of argument which is foreign to our ears. For example, here is a short speech of Simplicius, the upholder of the old Aristotelian tradition in Galileo's Dialogues, chosen almost at random:—

Aristotle, though of a very perspicacious wit, would not strain it further than needed: holding in all his argumentations, that sensible experiments were to be preferred before any reasons founded upon strength of wit, and said those which should deny the testimony of sense deserved to be punished with the loss of that sense; now who is so blind, that sees not the parts of the Earth and Water to move, as being grave, naturally downwards, namely, towards the centre of the Universe, assigned by nature herself for the end and term of right motion *deorsum;* and doth not likewise see the Fire and Air to move right upwards towards the Concave of the Lunar Orb, as to the natural end of motion *sursum?* And this being so manifestly seen, and we being certain, that *eadem est ratio totius et partium,* why may we not assert it for a true and manifest proposition, that the natural motion of the Earth is the right motion *ad medium,* and that of the Fire, the right *a medio?*

In this passage we note that different functions are assigned to the Centre of the Universe to which the Earth or any part of it naturally moves in a straight line, and to the Concave of the Lunar Orb (to which Fire naturally moves in a straight line). The idea of the neutrality of situation and the universality of physical laws, regulating casual occurrences and holding indifferently in every part, is entirely absent. On the contrary, each local part of nature has its one peculiar function in the scheme of things. It is a fine conception: the only objection to it is that it does not seem to be true. I am not sure, however, that the Einstein conception of the physical forces as being due to the contortions of space-time is not in some respects a return to it.

But let us see how Galileo in the person of the interlocutor, Salviatus, answers this speech of Simplicius. His answer is somewhat long, and I only give the relevant part:—

. . . Now, like as from the consentaneous conspiration of all the parts of the Earth to form its whole, doth follow, that they with equal inclination concur thither from all parts; and to unite themselves as much as is possible together, they there physically adapt themselves; why may we not believe that the Sun, Moon, and other mundane Bodies, be also of a round figure, not by other than a concordant instinct, and natural concourse of all the parts composing them? Of which, if any, at any time, by any violence were separated from the whole, is it not reasonable to think, that they would spontaneously and by natural instinct return? and in this manner to infer, that the right motion agreeth with all mundane bodies alike.

Note that in this answer Galileo, in the person of Salviatus, entirely ignores any peculiar function or property to be assigned to a Centre of the Universe or to a Concave of the Lunar Orb. He has in his mind the conceptions of modern science, in that the Earth, the Moon, the Sun, and the other planets are all bodies moving in an indifferent neutral space, and each attracting its own parts to form its whole—or, as Salviatus puts it, "the consentaneous conspiration of all the parts of the Earth to form its whole."

Evidently Galileo is very near to the Newtonian doctrine of Universal Gravitation. But he is not quite there. Newton enunciates the doctrine that every particle of matter attracts every other particle of matter in a certain definite way. Galileo—as children say in the game of Hide-and-Seek—is very hot in respect to this doctrine. But he does not seem, at least in this passage, to have made the final generalization. He is thinking particularly of the Earth, the Sun, the Moon, and other planets— and his guardian angel does not appear to have whispered to him the generalization "any material body." Newton probably knew Galileo's Dialogues nearly by heart. They were standard works in his time. Cannot we imagine him sitting in his rooms between the gateway and the chapel of Trinity College, or in the orchard watching the apple fall, and with this passage of Galileo's

Dialogue running in his mind, perhaps the very words of Salusbury's translation which I have quoted, "the consentaneous conspiration of all the parts of the Earth to form its whole." Suddenly the idea flashes on him— "What are the Earth and the Sun and the Moon? Why, they are any bodies! We should say therefore that any bodies attract. But if this be the case, the Earth and the Sun and the Moon attract each other, and we have the cause maintaining the planets in their orbits." In this course of thought Newton would have been assisted by his third law of motion. For by it if the Earth attracts the apple, then the apple attracts the Earth.

By this conjectural reconstruction of Newton's state of mind we see that, given a genius with adequate mathematical faculties, Newton's Principia is the next step in science after Galileo's Dialogues. Probably Galileo himself would have gone farther in this direction if his imagination had not been hampered by the necessity of arguing with the Conservative Party. It is in general a mistake to waste time in discussions with people who have the wrong ideas in their heads. But in Galileo's time and country the Conservative Party had thumb-screws at its service and could thereby enforce a certain amount of attention to its ideas.

Undoubtedly the whole implication of the answer of Salviatus is that the Earth, Sun, etcetera, are mere bits of matter. It is difficult for us to estimate how great an advance Galileo made in adumbrating this position. Consider, for example, this statement by Simplicius, made in another connection, enforcing a doctrine which he upholds throughout the whole of the Dialogues:—

See here for a beginning, two most convincing arguments to demonstrate the Earth to be most different from the Cælestial bodies. First, the bodies that are generable, corruptible, alterable, &c., are quite different from those that are ingenerable, incorruptible, unalterable, &c. But the Earth is generable, corruptible, alterable, &c., and the Cælestial bodies ingenerable, incorruptible, unalterable, &c. Therefore the Earth is quite different from the Cælestial bodies.

That is the sort of thing that Galileo was up against, not as a mere casual idea occurring to a subtle reasoner, but as the very texture of current notions. The primary achievement of the first physical synthesis was to clear all this away. Galileo with his telescope, his trenchant, bold intellect, and his magnificent physical intuition was the man who did it.

But we have not nearly exhausted Galileo's contributions to the general ideas of science. We owe to Galileo the First Law of Motion. Probably most of us have in our minds Newton's enunciation of this law, "Every body continues in its state of rest or of uniform motion in a straight line except so far as it is compelled by impressed force to change that state." This is the first article of the creed of science; and like the Church's creeds it is more than a mere statement of belief: it is a pæan of triumph over defeated heretics. It should be set to music and chanted in the halls of Universities. The defeated adversaries are the Aristotelians who for two thousand years imposed on Dynamics the search for a physical cause of motion, whereas the true doctrine conceives uniform motion in a straight line as a state in which every body will naturally continue except so far as it is compelled by impressed force to change that state. Accordingly in Dynamics we search for a cause of the change of motion, namely either a change in respect to speed or a change in respect to direction of motion. For example, an Aristotelian investigating the motion of the planets in their orbits would seek for tangential forces to keep the planets moving; but a follower of Galileo seeks for normal forces to deflect the direction of motion along the curved orbit. This is why Newton, at the moment which we pictured him as he sat in his rooms in Trinity College thinking about gravitation, at once saw that the attraction of the Sun was the required force. It was nearly normal to the orbits of the planets. Here again we see how immediately Newton's physical ideas follow from those of Galileo. One genius completes the work of the other.

It has been stated by Whewell that in his Dialogues

on the Two Principal Systems of the World Galileo does not enunciate the first law of motion, and that it only appears in his subsequent Dialogues on Mechanics. This may be formally true so far as a neat decisive statement is concerned. But in essence the first law of motion is presupposed in the argumentation of the earlier dialogues. The whole explanation why loose things are not left behind as the Earth moves depends upon it.

Galileo also prepared the way for Newton's final enunciation of the Laws of Motion by his masterly investigation of the uniform acceleration of falling bodies on the Earth's surface and his demonstration that this acceleration is independent of the relative weights of the bodies, except so far as extraneous retarding forces are concerned. He swept away the old classification of natural and violent motions as founded on trivial unessential differences, and left the way entirely open for Newton's final generalizations. Newton conceived explicitly the idea of a neutral absolute space within which all motion is to be construed, and of mass as a permanent intrinsic physical quantity associated with matter, unalterable except by the destruction of matter. He phrased this concept in the definition, mass is quantity of matter. He then conceived the true measure of force as being the product of the mass of the body into its rate of change of velocity. The importance of this conception lies in the fact that force as thus conceived is found to depend on simple physical conditions, such as mass, electric and magnetic charges, electric currents, and distances. We owe to Newton the final formulation of the basic physical ideas which have served science so well during these last two centuries. They comprise the foundations of the science of Dynamics, and Law of Gravitation. We also owe to Galileo's experimental genius the telescope and its first systematic use in science, the pendulum clock (subsequently perfected by Huyghens) and the experimental demonstration of the laws of falling bodies. To Newton's mathematical genius we owe the deduction of the properties of the planetary orbits from dynamical principles. To Galileo and Newton we must add the name of Kepler so far as astronomy is concerned, and of Stevinus of Bruges so far as mechanics is concerned. He discovered the famous triangle of forces. But in one lecture lasting one hour you will not expect me to give a detailed account of the science of the seventeenth century.

In like manner we must add the name of Huyghens in mentioning the services of Galileo and Newton to the science of Optics. Huyghens first suggested the undulatory theory of light, to be revived at the beginning of the nineteenth century by Thomas Young and Fresnel. But the immediately fruitful work was due to Galileo with his studies on the theory of the telescope, and to Newton with his studies on the theory of colour. Both Dynamics and Optics reached Galileo as a series of detached truths (or falsehoods) loosely connected. After the work of Galileo and Newton they emerged as wellknit sciences on firm foundations.

Galileo's preoccupation with Optics doubtless helped him to another great idea which has coloured all modern thought. Light is transmitted through space from its origin by paths which may be devious and broken. What you see depends on the light as it enters your eye. You may see a green leaf behind the looking-glass; but the leaf is really behind your head and you are really looking at its image in the mirror. Thus the green which you see is not the property of the leaf, but it is the result of the stimulation of the nerves of the retina by the light which enters the eye. These considerations led Descartes and Locke to elaborate the idea of external nature consisting of matter moving in space and with merely primary qualities. These primary qualities are its shape, its degree of hardness and cohesiveness, its massiveness, and its attractive effects and its resilience. Our perceptions of nature such as colour, sound, taste and smell, and sensations of heat and cold form the secondary qualities. These secondary qualities are merely mental projections which are the result of the stimulation of the brain by the appropriate nerves. Such in outline is the famous theory of primary and secondary qualities in the form in which it has held the field during the modern period of science. It has been of essential service in directing scientific investigation into fruitful fields both of physics and physiology. Now the credit for its first sketch is due to Galileo. Here is an extract from Galileo's work, *Il Saggiatore,* published in 1624. I take it from the English life of Galileo by J. J. Fahie:—

"I have now only to fulfill my promise of declaring my opinions on the proposition that motion is the cause of heat, and to explain in what manner it appears to me that it may be true. But I must first make some remarks on that which we call heat, since I strongly suspect that a notion of it prevails which is very remote from the truth; for it is believed that there is a true accident, affection, or quality, really inherent in the substance by which we feel ourselves heated. This much I have to say, that as soon as I form a conception of a material or corporeal substance, I simultaneously feel the necessity of conceiving that it has boundaries, and is of some shape or other; that relatively to others it is great or small; that it is in this or that place, in this or that time; that it is in motion or at rest; that it touches, or does not touch another body; that it is unique, rare, or common; nor can I, by any act of imagination, disjoin it from these qualities; but I do not find myself absolutely compelled to apprehend it as necessarily accompanied by such conditions as that it must be white or red, bitter or sweet, sonorous or silent, smelling sweetly or disagreeably; and if the senses had not pointed out these qualities, it is probable that language and imagination alone could never have arrived at them. Therefore I am inclined to think that these tastes, smells, colours, &c., with regard to the object in which they appear to reside, are nothing more than mere names, and exist only in the sensitive body; insomuch that when the living creature is removed, all these qualities are carried off and annihilated; although we have imposed particular names upon them (different from those other and real accidents), and would fain persuade ourselves that they truly and in fact exist. But I do not believe that there exists anything in external bodies for exciting tastes, smells and sounds, but size, shape, quantity, and motion, swift or slow; and if ears, tongues, and noses were removed, I am of opinion that shape, quantity, and motion would remain, but there would be an end of smells, tastes, and sounds, which, abstractedly from the living creature, I take to be mere words."

If we knew nothing else about Galileo except that in the October of the year 1623 he published this extract, we should know for certain that a man of the highest philosophic genius then existed. On the subject of this extract, he leaves nothing for Descartes and Locke to do, except to repeat his statement in their own language, and to emphasize its philosophic importance. Indeed in many ways this original statement by Galileo is, as I believe, more accurately and carefully drawn than the usual formulations of modern times which I followed in my introductory remark.

I will now quit the special consideration of Galileo and Newton. I hope that I have with sufficient clearness given my reasons for holding that they are to be considered as the parents of modern science and as the joint authors of the first physical synthesis. You cannot disentangle their work. There would have been no Newton without Galileo; and it is hardly a paradox to say, that there would have been no Galileo without Newton. Galileo was the Julius Cæsar and Newton the Augustus Cæsar of the empire of science.

But these men did not work in a vacuum. It was an age of ferment, and they had as contemporaries men with genius all but equal to theirs. Francis Bacon was a contemporary of Galileo, somewhat older (1561-1626). I need not remind you that Bacon was the apostle of the experimental method. He especially emphasized the importance of keeping our minds open throughout a careful and prolonged examination of the facts. Like all apostles he somewhat exaggerated his message, and perhaps undervalued the importance of provisional theories. But the main point is perfectly correct and particularly important in view of the tradition of the preceding 1500 years, during which experiment had languished. Aristotle had discovered the importance of classification, and neither he nor his followers had realized the danger of classification proceeding on slight and trivial grounds. The greatest curse to the progress of science is a hasty classification based on trivialities. An example of what I mean is Aristotle's classification of motions into violent and natural. Bacon's writings were a continual protest against this pitfall. Again the active life of Descartes lies between those of Galileo and Newton. He published his *Principia Philosophiae* in 1644, just two years after the date which I have assigned as the symbolic centre of the epoch. The general concepts of space and matter, body and spirit, as they have permeated the scientific world, are largely in accordance with the way in which he fashioned them. He viewed space as a property of matter and therefore rejected the idea of purely empty space. This conception of space as an essential plenum led him to speculate on the other physical characteristics of the stuff whose extension is space. He thus hit on the idea of the vortices which carry along the heavenly bodies. These vortices are a failure. For one thing, they show that Descartes had not really assimilated the full import of Galileo's work in his discovery of the first law of motion. The planets do not want anything to carry them along, and that is just what Descartes provides. But for all that I hold that Descartes with his plenum was groping towards a very important truth which I will endeavour to explain before I finish this lecture. Newton's formulation of gravitation led Newton's followers to insist on the possibility of a vacuum, but the nineteenth century again filled space with an ether. Finally Einstein has recurred to the inversion of Descartes' doctrine and has made matter a property of space. The Newtonian vacuum and the Cartesian plenum have fought a very equal duel during the last few centuries. Leibniz, Newton's contemporary, emphasized the relativity of space.

This mention of relativity leads me to my last topic, which is to ask, how to-day we would criticize this First

Physical Synthesis which we owe to the seventeenth century.

In the first place, if we are wise, before criticizing it we will stop to admire it, and to note its essential services to science, and (in its main outlines) its continuing value to-day. We must do honour to the century of genius to which we owe it—a century which will compare with the greatest that Greece can show.

By a criticism of the great physical synthesis which is the legacy of this century to science I do not mean a mere enumeration of the additions since made, for example, the rise of the concept of energy, of the atomic theory, or of the theory of various chemical elements. Such homogeneous additions leave the concept undisturbed. In this way, Kelvin made it the mainspring of all his scientific speculations. But for the last thirty years or so, the great ideas of the seventeenth century have, so to speak, been losing their dominating grip on physical science.

Clerk-Maxwell probably thought that he had finally established its ascendancy. In truth he had set going trains of thought which in the hands of his followers have caused it to totter. Galileo and his followers thought in terms of time, space, and matter. They were in fact more Aristotelian than they knew—though they wore their Aristotle with a difference. Clerk-Maxwell emphasized the importance of the electromagnetic field as an interplay of relations between various electromagnetic quantities. Maxwell himself looked on this field as merely expressing strains, stresses, and motions of the ether, a point of view quite in the Galilean tradition. But recently the field itself has come to be conceived as the ultimate fact, and properties of matter have been explained in terms of it. Thus energy, mass, matter, chemical elements are now expressed as electromagnetic phenomena. The ether is still there for those who like it, but it merely serves to allay the tortures of a metaphysical craving.

But Einstein and Minkowski have gone farther. Hitherto time and space have been treated as separate

66

and independent factors in the scheme of things. They have combined them. This is a complete refashioning of older ideas and is in many ways much more consonant with the Cartesian point of view.

The world as we observe it involves process and extension. Hitherto process has been identified with serial time, and extension with space. But this neglects the fact that there is an extension of time. Conceive any ultimate concrete fact as an extended process. If you have lost process or lost extension, you know that you are dealing with abstraction. What is going on here in this room is extended process. Extension and process are each abstractions. But these abstractions can be made in different ways. The space which we apprehend as extension without process and the time which we apprehend as serial process without spatial extension are not each unique. In different circumstances we affix different meanings to the notion of space, and different meanings to the correlative notion of time. In respect to space there is no paradox in this assertion. For us the space of this room is a definite volume; for a man in the sun the room is sweeping through space. But it is paradoxical to hold that the serial process which we apprehend as time is different from the serial process which the man in the sun apprehends as time. Yet if you do that, you can introduce mathematical formulæ expressing spatio-temporal measurements which at one sweep explain a whole multitude of perplexing scientific observation. In fact the formulæ practically have to be admitted, and the theory is the simplest explanation of them. Also philosophically the closer association of time and space is a great advantage.

We now come back to Descartes. He conceived extension as essentially a quality of matter. Generalize his idea: the ultimate fact is not static matter but the flux of physical existence: call any part of this flux, with all its fullness of content and happening, an event: extension is essentially a quality of events and so is process. But the becomingness of nature is not to be constricted within one serial linear procession of time. It requires an indefinite number of such processions to express the complete vision.

If this line of thought, which is that underlying the modern relativity, be admitted, the whole synthesis of the seventeenth century has to be recast. Its Time, its Space, and its Matter are in the melting-pot—and there we must leave them.

Axioms of Geometry

THEORIES OF SPACE

UNTIL THE DISCOVERY of the non-Euclidean geometries (Lobatchewsky, 1826 and 1829; J. Bolyai, 1832; B. Riemann, 1854), geometry was universally considered as being exclusively the science of existent space. (See section VI *Non-Euclidean Geometry*.) In respect to the science, as thus conceived, two controversies may be noticed. First, there is the controversy respecting the absolute and relational theories of space. According to the absolute theory, which is the traditional view (held explicitly by Newton), space has an existence, in some sense whatever it may be, independent of the bodies which it contains. The bodies occupy space, and it is not intrinsically unmeaning to say that any definite body occupies *this* part of space, and not *that* part of space, without reference to other bodies occupying space. According to the relational theory of space, of which the chief exponent was Leibniz,[1] space is nothing but a certain assemblage of the relations between the various particular bodies in space. The idea of space with no bodies in it is absurd. Accordingly there can be no meaning in saying that a body is *here* and not *there,* apart from a reference to the other bodies in the universe. Thus, on this theory, absolute motion is intrinsically unmeaning. It is admitted on all hands that in practice only relative motion is directly measurable.

[1] For an analysis of Leibniz's ideas on space, cf. B. Russell, *The Philosophy of Leibniz,* chs. viii-x.

Newton, however, maintains in the *Principia* (scholium to the 8th definition) that it is indirectly measurable by means of the effects of "centrifugal force" as it occurs in the phenomena of rotation. This irrelevance of absolute motion (if there be such a thing) to science has led to the general adoption of the relational theory by modern men of science. But no decisive argument for either view has at present been elaborated.[2] Kant's view of space as being a form of perception at first sight appears to cut across this controversy. But he, saturated as he was with the spirit of the Newtonian physics, must (at least in both editions of the *Critique*) be classed with the upholders of the absolute theory. The form of perception has a type of existence proper to itself independently of the particular bodies which it contains. For example, he writes:[3]

"Space does not represent any quality of objects by themselves, or objects in their relation to one another, i.e., space does not represent any determination which is inherent in the objects themselves, and would remain, even if all subjective conditions of intuition were removed."

AXIOMS

The second controversy is that between the view that the axioms applicable to space are known only from experience, and the view that in some sense these axioms are given *a priori*. Both these views, thus broadly stated, are capable of various subtle modifications, and a discussion of them would merge into a general treatise on epistemology. The cruder forms of the *a priori* view have been made quite untenable by the modern mathematical discoveries. Geometers now profess ignorance in many respects of the exact axioms which apply to

[2] Cf. Hon. Bertrand Russell, "Is Position in Time and Space Absolute or Relative?" *Mind,* n.s. vol. 10 (1901), and A. N. Whitehead, "Mathematical Concepts of the Material World," *Phil. Trans.* (1906), p. 205.

[3] Cf. *Critique of Pure Reason,* 1st section; "Of Space." conclusion A, Max Müller's translation.

existent space, and it seems unlikely that a profound study of the question should thus obliterate *a priori* intuitions.

Another question irrelevant to this article, but with some relevance to the above controversy, is that of the derivation of our perception of existent space from our various types of sensation. This is a question for psychology.[4]

Definition of Abstract Geometry.—Existent space is the subject matter of only one of the applications of the modern science of abstract geometry, viewed as a branch of pure mathematics. Geometry has been defined [5] as "the study of series of two or more dimensions." It has also been defined [6] as "the science of cross classification." These definitions are founded upon the actual practice of mathematicians in respect to their use of the term "Geometry." Either of them brings out the fact that geometry is not a science with a determinate subject matter. It is concerned with any subject matter to which the formal axioms may apply. Geometry is not peculiar in this respect. All branches of pure mathematics deal merely with types of relations. Thus the fundamental ideas of geometry (e.g., those of *points* and of *straight lines*) are not ideas of determinate entities, but of any entities for which the axioms are true. And a set of formal geometrical axioms cannot in themselves be true or false, since they are not determinate propositions, in that they do not refer to a determinate subject matter. The axioms are propositional functions.[7] When a set of axioms is given, we can ask (1) whether they are consistent, (2) whether their "existence theorem" is proved, (3) whether they are independent. Axioms are consistent when the contradictory of any axiom cannot

---

[4] Cf. Ernst Mach, *Erkenntniss und Irrtum* (Leipzig); the relevant chapters are translated by T. J. McCormack, *Space and Geometry* (London, 1906); also A. Meinong, *Über die Stellung der Gegenstandstheorie im System der Wissenschaften* (Leipzig, 1907).

[5] Cf. Russell, *Principles of Mathematics*, § 352 (Cambridge, 1903).

[6] Cf. A. N. Whitehead, *The Axioms of Projective Geometry*, § 3 (Cambridge, 1906).

[7] Cf. Russell, *Princ. of Math.*, ch. i.

71

be deduced from the remaining axioms. Their existence theorem is the proof that they are true when the fundamental ideas are considered as denoting some determinate subject matter, so that the axioms are developed into determinate propositions. It follows from the logical law of contradiction that the proof of the existence theorem proves also the consistency of the axioms. This is the only method of proof of consistency. The axioms of a set are independent of each other when no axiom can be deduced from the remaining axioms of the set. The independence of a given axiom is proved by establishing the consistency of the remaining axioms of the set, together with the contradictory of the given axiom. The enumeration of the axioms is simply the enumeration of the hypotheses[8] (with respect to the undetermined subject matter) of which some at least occur in each of the subsequent propositions.

Any science is called a "geometry" if it investigates the theory of the classification of a set of entities (the points) into classes (the straight lines), such that (1) there is one and only one class which contains any given pair of entities, and (2) every such class contains more than two members. In the two geometries, important from their relevance to existent space, axioms which secure an order of the points on any line also occur. These geometries will be called "Projective Geometry" and "Descriptive Geometry." In projective geometry any two straight lines in a plane intersect, and the straight lines are closed series which return into themselves, like the circumference of a circle. In descriptive geometry two straight lines in a plane do not necessarily intersect, and a straight line is an open series without beginning or end. Ordinary Euclidean geometry is a descriptive geometry; it becomes a projective geometry when the so-called "points at infinity" are added.

Projective Geometry

Projective geometry may be developed from two undefined fundamental ideas, namely, that of a "point"

[8] Cf. Russell, *loc. cit.*, and G. Frege, "Über die Grundlagen der Geometrie," *Jahresber. der Deutsch. Math. Ver.* (1906).

and that of a "straight line." These undetermined ideas take different specific meanings for the various specific subject matters to which projective geometry can be applied. The number of the axioms is always to some extent arbitrary, being dependent upon the verbal forms of statement which are adopted. They will be presented [9] here as twelve in number, eight being "axioms of classification," and four being "axioms of order."

Axioms of Classification.—The eight axioms of classification are as follows:

1. Points form a class of entities with at least two members.

2. Any straight line is a class of points containing at least three members.

3. Any two distinct points lie in one and only one straight line.

4. There is at least one straight line which does not contain all the points.

5. If A, B, C are non-collinear points, and A′ is on the straight line BC, and B′ is on the straight line CA, then the straight line AA′ and BB′ possess a point in common.

Definition.—If A, B, C are any three non-collinear points, the *plane* ABC is the class of points lying on the straight lines joining A with the various points on the straight line BC.

6. There is at least one plane which does not contain all the points.

7. There exists a plane α, and a point A not incident in α, such that any point lies in some straight line which contains both A and a point in α.

Definition.—Harm. (ABCD) symbolizes the following conjoint statements: (1) that the points A, B, C, D are collinear, and (2) that a quadrilateral can be found with

[9] This formulation—though not in respect to number—is in all essentials that of M. Pieri, cf. "I principii della Geometria di Posizione," *Accad. R. di Torino* (1898); also cf. Whitehead, *loc. cit.*

one pair of opposite sides intersecting at A, with the other pair intersecting at C, and with its diagonals passing through B and D respectively. Then B and D are said to be "harmonic conjugates" with respect to A and C.

8. Harm. (ABCD) implies that B and D are distinct points.

In the above axioms 4 secures at least two dimensions, axiom 5 is the fundamental axiom of the plane, axiom 6 secures at least three dimensions, and axiom 7 secures at most three dimensions. From axioms 1-5 it can be proved that any two distinct points in a straight line determine that line, that any three non-collinear points in a plane determine that plane, that the straight line containing any two points in a plane lies wholly in that plane, and that any two straight lines in a plane intersect. From axioms 1-6 Desargues's well-known theorem on triangles in perspective can be proved.

The enunciation of this theorem is as follows: if ABC and A'B'C' are two coplanar triangles such that the lines AA', BB', CC' are concurrent, then the three points of intersection of BC and B'C' of CA and C'A', and of AB and A'B' are collinear; and conversely if the three points of intersection are collinear, the three lines are concurrent. The proof which can be applied is the usual projective proof by which a third triangle A''B''C'' is constructed not coplanar with the other two, but in perspective with each of them.

It has been proved[10] that Desargues's theorem cannot be deduced from axioms 1-5, that is, if the geometry be confined to two dimensions. All the proofs proceed by the method of producing a specification of "points" and "straight lines" which satisfies axioms 1-5, and such that Desargues's theorem does not hold.

[10] Cf. G. Peano, "Sui fondamenti della Geometria," p. 73, *Rivista di matematica,* vol. iv (1894), and D. Hilbert, *Grundlagen der Geometrie* (Leipzig, 1899); and R. F. Moulton, "A Simple non-Desarguesian Plane Geometry," *Trans. Amer. Math. Soc.,* vol. iii (1902).

It follows from axioms 1-5 that Harm. (ABCD) implies Harm. (ADCB) and Harm. (CBAD), and that, if A, B, C be any three distinct collinear points, there exists at least one point D such that Harm. (ABCD). But it requires Desargues's theorem, and hence axiom 6, to prove that Harm. (ABCD) and Harm. (ABCD') imply the identity of D and D'.

The necessity for axiom 8 has been proved by G. Fano,[11] who has produced a three dimensional geometry of fifteen points, i.e., a method of cross classification of fifteen entities, in which each straight line contains three points, and each plane contains seven straight lines. In this geometry axiom 8 does not hold. Also from axioms 1-6 and 8 it follows that Harm. (ABCD) implies Harm. (BCDA).

Definitions.—When two plane figures can be derived from one another by a single projection, they are said to be in *perspective.* When two plane figures can be derived one from the other by a finite series of perspective relations between intermediate figures they are said to be *projectively* related. Any property of a plane figure which necessarily also belongs to any projectively related figure, is called a *projective* property.

The following theorem, known from its importance as "the fundamental theorem of projective geometry," cannot be proved [12] from axioms 1-8. The enunciation is: "A projective correspondence between the points on two straight lines is completely determined when the correspondents of three distinct points on one line are determined on the other." This theorem is equivalent[13] (assuming axioms 1-8) to another theorem, known as

[11] Cf. "Sui postulati fondamentali della geometria projettiva," *Giorn. di matematica,* vol. xxx (1891) ; also of Pieri, *loc. cit.,* and Whitehead, *loc. cit.*

[12] Cf. Hilbert, *loc. cit.;* for a fuller exposition of Hilbert's proof cf. K. T. Vahlen, *Abstrakte Geometrie* (Leipzig, 1905) , also Whitehead, *loc. cit.*

[13] Cf. H. Wiener, *Jahresber. der Deutsch. Math. Ver.* vol. i (1890); and F. Schur, "Uber den Fundamentalsatz der projectiven Geometrie," *Math. Ann.* vol. li (1899).

Pappus's Theorem, namely: "If l and l' are two distinct coplanar lines, and A, B, C are three distinct points on l, and A', B' C' are three distinct points on l', then the three points of intersection AA' and B'C, of A'B and CC', of BB' and C'A, are collinear." This theorem is obviously Pascal's well-known theorem respecting a hexagon inscribed in a conic, for the special case when the conic has degenerated into the two lines l and l'. Another theorem also equivalent (assuming axioms 1-8) to the fundamental theorem is the following:[14] If the three collinear pairs of points, A and A', B and B', C and C', are such that the three pairs of opposite sides of a complete quadrangle pass respectively through them, i.e. one pair through A and A' respectively, and so on, and if also the three sides of the quadrangle which pass through A, B, and C, are concurrent in one of the corners of the quadrangle, then another quadrangle can be found with the same relation to the three pairs of points, except that its three sides which pass through A, B, and C, are not concurrent.

Thus, if we choose to take any one of these three theorems as an axiom, all the theorems of projective geometry which do not require ordinal or metrical ideas for their enunciation can be proved. Also a conic can be defined as the locus of the points found by the usual construction, based on Pascal's theorem, for points on the conic through five given points. But it is unnecessary to assume here any one of the suggested axioms; for the fundamental theorem can be deduced from the axioms of order together with axioms 1-8.

Axioms of Order.—It is possible to define (cf. Pieri, *loc. cit.*) the property upon which the order of points on a straight line depends. But to secure that this property does in fact range the points in a serial order, some axioms are required. A straight line is to be a closed series; thus, when the points are in order, it requires two points on the line to divide it into two distinct complementary segments, which do not overlap, and

[14] Cf. Hilbert, *loc. cit.*, and Whitehead, *loc. cit.*

together form the whole line. Accordingly the problem of the definition of order reduces itself to the definition of these two segments formed by any two points on the line; and the axioms are stated relatively to these segments.

Definitions.—If A, B, C are three collinear points, the points on the *segment ABC* are defined to be those points such as X, for which there exist two points Y and Y′ with the property that Harm. (AYCY′) and Harm. (BYXY′) both hold. The *supplementary segment ABC* is defined to be the rest of the points on the line. This definition is elucidated by noticing that with our ordinary geometrical ideas, if B and X are any two points between A and C, then the two pairs of points, A and C, B and X, define an involution with real double points, namely, the Y and Y′ of the above definition. The property of belonging to a segment ABC is projective, since the harmonic relation is projective.

The first three axioms of order (cf. Pieri, *loc. cit.*) are:

9. If A, B, C are three distinct collinear points, the supplementary segment ABC is contained within the segment BCA.

10. If A, B, C are three distinct collinear points, the common part of the segments BCA and CAB is contained in the supplementary segment ABC.

11. If A, B, C are three distinct collinear points, and D lies in the segment ABC, then the segment ADC is contained within the segment ABC.

From these axioms all the usual properties of a closed order follow. It will be noticed that, if A, B, C are any three collinear points, C is necessarily traversed in passing from A to B by one route along the line, and is not traversed in passing from A to B along the other route. Thus there is no meaning, as referred to closed straight lines, in the simple statement that C lies between A and B. But there may be a relation of separation between two pairs of collinear points, such as A and C, and B and D. The couple B and D is said to separate A and C, if the four points are collinear and D lies in the segment complementary to the segment ABC. The property of the separation of pairs of points by pairs of points is projective. Also it can be proved that Harm. (ABCD) implies that B and D separate A and C.

Definitions.—A series of entities arranged in a serial order, open or closed, is said to be *compact,* if the series contains no immediately consecutive entities, so that in traversing the series from any one entity to any other entity it is necessary to pass through entities distinct from either. It was the merit of R. Dedekind and of G. Cantor explicitly to formulate another fundamental property of series. The Dedekind property[15] as applied to an open series can be defined thus: An open series possesses the Dedekind property, if, however, it be divided into two mutually exclusive classes u and v, which (1) contain between them the whole series, and (2) are such that every member of u precedes in the serial order every member of v, there is always a member of the series, belonging to one of the two, u or v, which precedes every member of v (other than itself if it belong to v), and also succeeds every member of u (other than itself if it belong to u). Accordingly in an open series with the Dedekind property there is always a member of the series marking the junction of two classes such as u and v. An open series is *continuous* if it is compact and possesses the Dedekind property. A closed series can always be transformed into an open series by taking any arbitrary member as the first term and by taking one of the two ways round as the ascending order of the series. Thus the definitions of compactness and of the Dedekind property can be at once transferred to a closed series.

12. The last axiom of order is that there exists at least one straight line for which the point order possesses the Dedekind property.

[15] Cf. Dedekind, *Stetigkeit und irrationale Zahlen* (1872).

78

It follows from axioms 1-12 by projection that the Dedekind property is true for all lines. Again the *harmonic system ABC*, where A, B, C are collinear points, is defined [16] thus: take the harmonic conjugates A', B', C' of each point with respect to the other two, again take the harmonic conjugates of each of the six points A, B, C, A', B', C' with respect to each pair of the remaining five, and proceed in this way by an unending series of steps. The set of points thus obtained is called the harmonic system ABC. It can be proved that a harmonic system is compact, and that every segment of the line containing it possesses members of it. Furthermore, it is easy to prove that the fundamental theorem holds for harmonic systems, in the sense that, if A, B, C are three points on a line *l*, and A', B', C' are three points on a line *l'*, and if by any two distinct series of projections, A, B, C are projected into A', B', C', then any point of the harmonic system ABC corresponds to the same point of the harmonic system A'B'C' according to both the projective relations which are thus established between *l* and *l'*. It now follows immediately that the fundamental theorem must hold for all the points on the lines *l* and *l'*, since (as has been pointed out) harmonic systems are "everywhere dense" on their containing lines. Thus the fundamental theorem follows from the axioms of order.

A system of numerical co-ordinates can now be introduced, possessing the property that linear equations represent planes and straight lines. The outline of the argument by which this remarkable problem (in that "distance" is as yet undefined) is solved, will now be given. It is first proved that the points on any line can in a certain way be definitely associated with all the positive and negative real numbers, so as to form with them a one-one correspondence. The arbitrary elements in the establishment of this relation are the points on the line associated with 0, 1 and ∞.

[16] Cf. v. Staudt, *Geometrie der Lage* (1847).

This association[17] is most easily effected by considering a class of projective relations of the line with itself, called by F. Schur (*loc. cit.*) *prospectivities*.

Let l be the given line, m and n any two lines intersecting at U on l, S and S' two points on n. Then a projective relation between l and itself is formed by projecting l from S on to m, and then by projecting m from S' back on to l. All such projective relations, however m, n, S and S' be varied, are called "prospectivities," and U is the double point of the prospectivity. If a point O on l is related to A by a prospectivity, then all prospectivities, which (1) have the same double point U, and (2) relate O to A, give the same correspondent (Q, in figure) to any point P on the line l; in fact they are all the same prospectivity, however m, n, S, and S' may have been varied subject to these conditions. Such a prospectivity will be denoted by (OAU^2).

The sum of two prospectivities, written $(OAU^2) + (OBU^2)$, is defined to be that transformation of the line l into itself which is obtained by first applying the prospectivity (OAU^2) and then applying the prospectivity (OBU^2). Such a transformation, when the two summands have the same double point, is itself a prospectivity with that double point.

With this definition of addition it can be proved that prospectivities with the same double point satisfy all the axioms of magnitude. Accordingly they can be associated in a one-one correspondence with the positive and negative real numbers. Let E be any point on l, distinct from O and U. Then the prospectivity (OEU^2) is associated with unity, the prospectivity (OOU^2) is associated with zero, and (OUU^2) with ∞. The prospectivities of the type (OPU^2), where P is any point on the segment OEU, correspond to the positive numbers; also

[17] Cf. Pasch, *Vorlesungen über neuere Geometrie* (Leipzig, 1882), a classic work; also Fiedler, *Die darstellende Geometrie* (1st ed., 1871, 3rd ed., 1888); Clebsch, *Vorlesungen über Geometrie*, vol. iii; Hilbert, *loc. cit.*; F. Schur, *Math. Ann.* Bd. lv (1902); Vahlen, *loc. cit.*; Whitehead, *loc. cit.*

if P′ is the harmonic conjugate of P with respect to O and U, the prospectivity $(OP'U^2)$ is associated with the corresponding negative number. Then any point P on l is associated with the same number as is the prospectivity (OPU^2).

It can be proved that the order of the numbers in algebraic order of magnitude agrees with the order on the line of the associated points. Let the numbers, assigned according to the preceding specification, be said to be associated with the points according to the "numeration-system (OEU)." The introduction of a co-ordinate system for a plane is now managed as follows: Take any triangle OUV in the plane, and on the lines OU and OV establish the numeration systems (OE_1U) and (OE_2V), where E_1 and E_2 are arbitrarily chosen. Then if M and N are associated with the numbers x and y according to these systems, the co-ordinates of P are x and y. It then follows that the equation of a straight line is of the form $ax + by + c = O$. Both co-ordinates of any point on the line UV are infinite. This can be avoided by introducing homogeneous co-ordinates X, Y, Z, where $x = X/Z$, and $y = Y/Z$, and $Z = O$ is the equation of UV.

The procedure for three dimensions is similar. Let OUVW be any tetrahedron, and associate points on OU, OV, OW with numbers according to the numeration systems (OE_1U), (OE_2V), and (OE_3W). Let the planes VWP, WUP, UVP cut OU, OV, OW in L, M, N respectively; and let x, y, z be the numbers associated with L, M, N respectively. Then P is the point (x, y, z). Also homogeneous co-ordinates can be introduced as before, thus avoiding the infinities on the plane UVW.

The cross ratio of a range of four collinear points can now be defined as a number characteristic of that range. Let the co-ordinates of any point P_r of the range $P_1\ P_2\ P_3\ P_4$ be

$$\frac{\lambda_r a + \mu_r + a'}{\lambda_r + \mu_r}, \ \frac{\lambda_r b + \mu_r b'}{\lambda_r + \mu_r}, \ \frac{\lambda_r c + \mu_r c'}{\lambda_r + \mu_r}, \ (r = 1,\ 2,\ 3,\ 4)$$

and let $(\lambda_r\mu_s)$ be written for $\lambda_r\mu_s-\lambda_s\mu_r$. Then the cross ratio $\{P_1 \ P_2 \ P_3 \ P_4\}$ is defined to be the number $(\lambda_1\mu_2)$ $(\lambda_3\mu_4)\,/\,(\lambda_1\mu_4)\ (\lambda_3\mu_2)$. The equality of the cross ratios of the ranges $(P_1 \ P_2 \ P_3 \ P_4)$ and $(Q_1 \ Q_2 \ Q_3 \ Q_4)$ is proved to be the necessary and sufficient condition for their mutual projectivity. The cross ratios of all harmonic ranges are then easily seen to be all equal to -1, by comparing with the range $(OE_1UE'_1)$ on the axis of x.

Thus all the ordinary propositions of geometry in which distance and angular measure do not enter otherwise in cross ratios can now be enunciated and proved. Accordingly the greater part of the analytical theory of conics and quadrics belongs to geometry at this stage. The theory of distance will be considered after the principles of descriptive geometry have been developed.

Descriptive Geometry

Descriptive geometry is essentially the science of multiple order for open series. The first satisfactory system of axioms was given by M. Pasch.[18] An improved version is due to G. Peano.[19] Both these authors treat the idea of the class of points constituting the segment lying *between* two points as an undefined fundamental idea. Thus in fact there are in this system two fundamental ideas, namely, of points and of segments. It is then easy enough to define the prolongations of the segments, so as to form the complete straight lines. D. Hilbert's[20] formulation of the axioms is in this respect practically based on the same fundamental ideas. His work is justly famous for some of the mathematical investigations contained in it, but his exposition of the axioms is distinctly inferior to that of Peano. Descriptive geometry can also be considered [21] as the science of a class of relations,

[18] Cf. *loc. cit.*

[19] Cf. *I Principii di geometria* (Turin, 1889) and "Sui fondamenti della geometria," *Rivista di mat.*, vol. iv (1894).

[20] Cf. *loc. cit.*

[21] Cf. Vailati, *Rivista di mat.*, vol. iv, and Russell, *loc. cit.* § 376.

each relation being a two-termed serial relation, as considered in the logic of relations, ranging the points between which it holds into a linear open order. Thus the relations are the straight lines, and the terms between which they hold are the points. But a combination of these two points of view yields[22] the simplest statement of all. Descriptive geometry is then conceived as the investigation of an undefined fundamental relation between three terms (points); and when the relation holds between three points A, B, C, the points are said to be "in the [linear] order ABC."

O. Veblen's axioms and definitions, slightly modified, are as follows:—

1. If the points A, B, C are in the order ABC, they are in the order CBA.

2. If the points A, B, C are in the order ABC, they are not in the order BCA.

3. If the points A, B, C are in the order ABC, A is distinct from C.

4. If A and B are any two distinct points, there exists a point C such that A, B, C are in the order ABC.

Definition.—The *line* AB ($A \pm B$) consists of A and B, and of all points X in one of the possible orders, ABX, AXB, XAB. The points X in the order AXB constitute the *segment* AB.

5. If points C and D ($C \pm D$) lie on the line AB, then A lies on the line CD.

6. There exist three distinct points A, B, C not in any of the orders ABC, BCA, CAB.

7. If three distinct points A, B, C do not lie on the same line, and D and E are two distinct points in the orders BCD and CEA, then a point F exists in the order AFB, and such that D, E, F are collinear.

Definition.—If A, B, C are three non-collinear points, the *plane* ABC is the class of points which lie on any one of the lines joining any two of the points belonging

[22] Cf. O. Veblen, "On the Projective Axioms of Geometry," *Trans. Amer. Math. Soc.,* vol. iii (1902).

to the boundary of the triangle ABC, the *boundary* being formed by the segments BC, CA and AB. The *interior* of the triangle ABC is formed by the points in segments such as PQ, where P and Q are points respectively on two of the segments BC, CA, AB.

8. There exists a plane ABC, which does not contain all the points.

Definition.—If A, B, C, D are four non-coplanar points, the space ABCD is the class of points which lie on any of the lines containing two points on the surface of the tetrahedron ABCD, the *surface* being formed by the interiors of the triangles ABC, BCD, DCA, DAB.

9. There exists a space ABCD which contains all the points.

10. The Dedekind property holds for the order of the points on any straight line.

It follows from axioms 1-9 that the points on any straight line are arranged in an open serial order. Also all the ordinary theorems respecting a point dividing a straight line into two parts, a straight line dividing a plane into two parts, and a plane dividing space into two parts, follow.

Again, in any plane α consider a line l and a point A.

Let any point B divide l into two half-lines l_1 and l_2. Then it can be proved that the set of half-lines, emanating from A and intersecting l_1 (such as m), are bounded by two half-lines, of which ABC is one. Let r be the other. Then it can be proved that r does not intersect l_1. Similarly for the half-line, such as n, intersecting l_2. Let s be its bounding half-line. Then two cases are possible. (1) The half-lines r and s are collinear, and together form one complete line. In this case, there is one and only one line (viz., $r + s$) through A and lying in α which does not intersect l. This is the Euclidean case, and the assumption that this case holds is the *Euclidean parallel axiom*. But (2) the half-lines r and s may not be collinear. In this case there will be an infinite number of lines, such as k for instance, containing A and lying in α, which do not intersect l. Then the lines through A in α are divided into two classes by reference to l, namely the *secant* lines which intersect l, and the *non-secant* lines which do not intersect l. The two boundary non-secant lines, of which r and s are respectively halves, may be called the two parallels to l through A.

The perception of the possibility of case 2 constituted the starting-point from which Lobatchewsky constructed the first explicit coherent theory of non-Euclidean geometry, and thus created a revolution in the philosophy of the subject. For many centuries the speculations of mathematicians on the foundations of geometry were almost confined to hopeless attempts to prove the "parallel axiom" without the introduction of some equivalent axiom.[23]

Associated Projective and Descriptive Spaces.—A region of a projective space, such that one, and only one, of the two supplementary segments between any pair of points within it lies entirely within it, satisfies the above axioms (1-10) of descriptive geometry, where the points of the region are the descriptive points, and the portions of straight lines within the region are the descriptive lines. If the excluded part of the original projective space is a single plane, the Euclidean parallel axiom also holds, otherwise it does not hold for the descriptive space of the limited region. Again, conversely, starting from an original descriptive space an associated projective space can be constructed by means of the concept of *ideal points*.[24] These are also called *projective points*, where it is understood that the simple points are the points of the original descriptive space. An *ideal point* is the class of straight lines which is composed of two coplanar lines a and b, together with the lines of inter-

[23] Cf. P. Stäckel and F. Engel, *Die Theorie der Parallellinien von Euklid bis auf Gauss* (Leipzig, 1895).

[24] Cf. Pasch, *loc. cit.*, and R. Bonola, "Sulla introduzione degli enti improprii in geometria projettive," *Giorn. di mat.* vol. xxxviii (1900); and Whitehead, *Axioms of Descriptive Geometry* (Cambridge, 1907).

section of all pairs of intersecting planes which respectively contain a and b, together with the lines of intersection with the plane ab of all planes containing any one of the lines (other than a or b) already specified as belonging to the ideal point. It is evident that, if the two original lines a and b intersect, the corresponding ideal point is nothing else than the whole class of lines which are concurrent at the point ab. But the essence of the definition is that an ideal point has an existence when the lines a and b do not intersect, so long as they are coplanar. An ideal point is termed *proper,* if the lines composing it intersect; otherwise it is *improper.*

A theorem essential to the whole theory is the following: if any two of the three lines a, b, c are coplanar, but the three lines are not all coplanar, and similarly for the lines a, b, d, then c and d are coplanar. It follows that any two lines belonging to an ideal point can be used as the pair of guiding lines in the definition. An ideal point is said to be *coherent* with a plane, if any of the lines composing it lie in the plane. An *ideal line* is the class of ideal points each of which is coherent with two given planes. If the planes intersect, the ideal line is termed *proper,* otherwise it is *improper.* It can be proved that any two planes, with which any two of the ideal points are both coherent, will serve as the guiding planes used in the definition. The ideal planes are defined as in projective geometry, and all the other definitions (for segments, order, etcetera) of projective geometry are applied to the ideal elements. If an ideal plane contains some proper ideal points, it is called *proper,* otherwise it is *improper.* Every ideal plane contains some improper ideal points.

It can now be proved that all the axioms of projective geometry hold of the ideal elements as thus obtained; and also that the order of the ideal points as obtained by the projective method agrees with the order of the proper ideal points as obtained from that of the associated points of the descriptive geometry. Thus a projective space has been constructed out of the ideal elements, and the proper ideal elements correspond element by element with the associated descriptive elements. Thus the proper ideal elements form a region in the projective space within which the descriptive axioms hold. Accordingly, by substituting ideal elements, a descriptive space can always be considered as a region within a projective space. This is the justification for the ordinary use of the "points at infinity" in the ordinary Euclidean geometry; the reasoning has been transferred from the original descriptive space to the associated projective space of ideal elements; and with the Euclidean parallel axiom the improper ideal elements reduce to the ideal points on a single improper ideal plane, namely, the plane at infinity.[25]

Congruence and Measurement.—The property of physical space which is expressed by the term "measurability" has now to be considered. This property has often been considered as essential to the very idea of space. For example, Kant writes,[26] "Space is represented as an infinite given *quantity*." This quantitative aspect of space arises from the measurability of distances, of angles, of surfaces and of volumes. These four types of quantity depend upon the two first among them as fundamental. The measurability of space is essentially connected with the idea of *congruence*, of which the simplest examples are to be found in the proofs of equality by the method of superposition, as used in elementary plane geometry. The mere concepts of "part" and of "whole" must of necessity be inadequate as the foundation of measurement, since we require the comparison as to quantity of regions of space which have no portions in common. The idea of congruence, as exemplified by the method of superposition in geometrical reasoning, appears to be founded upon that of the "rigid body," which moves from one position to another with its internal spatial relations unchanged. But unless there is a previous con-

[25] The original idea (confined to this particular case) of ideal points is due to von Staudt (*loc. cit.*).
[26] Cf. *Critique,* "Trans. Aesth." Sect. 1.

cept of the metrical relations between the parts of the body, there can be no basis from which to deduce that they are unchanged.

It would therefore appear as if the idea of the congruence, or metrical equality, of two portions of space (as empirically suggested by the motion of rigid bodies) must be considered as a fundamental idea incapable of definition in terms of those geometrical concepts which have already been enumerated. This was in effect the point of view of Pasch.[27] It has, however, been proved by Sophus Lie[28] that congruence is capable of definition without recourse to a new fundamental idea. This he does by means of his theory of finite continuous groups (see GROUPS, THEORY OF), of which the definition is possible in terms of our established geometrical ideas, remembering that co-ordinates have already been introduced. The displacement of a rigid body is simply a mode of defining to the senses a one-one transformation of all space into itself. For at any point of space a particle may be conceived to be placed, and to be rigidly connected with the rigid body; and thus there is a definite correspondence of any point of space with the new point occupied by the associated particle after displacement. Again two successive displacements of a rigid body from position A to position B, and from position B to position C, are the same in effect as one displacement from A to C. But this is the characteristic "group" property. Thus the transformations of space into itself defined by displacements of rigid bodies form a group.

Call this group of transformations a congruence-group. Now according to Lie a congruence-group is defined by the following characteristics:—

1. A congruence-group is a finite continuous group of one-one transformations, containing the identical transformation.

2. It is a sub-group of the general projective group, i.e. of the group of which any transformation converts

[27] Cf. *loc. cit.*

[28] Cf. *Über die Grundlagen der Geometrie* (Leipzig, *Ber.*, 1890); and *Theorie der Transformationsgruppen* (Leipzig, 1893), vol. iii.

planes into planes, and straight lines into straight lines.

3. An infinitesimal transformation can always be found satisfying the condition that, at least throughout a certain enclosed region, any definite line and any definite point on the line are latent, i.e., correspond to themselves.

4. No infinitesimal transformation of the group exists, such that, at least in the region for which (3) holds, a straight line, a point on it, and a plane through it, shall be latent.

The property enunciated by conditions (3) and (4), taken together, is named by Lie "Free mobility in the infinitesimal." Lie proves the following theorems for a projective space:—

1. If the above four conditions are only satisfied by a group throughout part of projective space, this part either (α) must be the region enclosed by a real closed quadric, or (β) must be the whole of the projective space with the exception of a single plane. In case (α) the corresponding congruence group is the continuous group for which the enclosing quadric is latent; and in case (β) an imaginary conic (with a real equation) lying in the latent plane is also latent, and the congruence group is the continuous group for which the plane and conic are latent.

2. If the above four conditions are satisfied by a group throughout the whole of projective space, the congruence group is the continuous group for which some imaginary quadric (with a real equation) is latent.

By a proper choice of non-homogeneous co-ordinates the equation of any quadrics of the types considered, either in theorem 1 (α), or in theorem 2, can be written in the form $1 + c(x^2 + y^2 + z^2) = 0$, where c is negative for a real closed quadric, and positive for an imaginary quadric. Then the general infinitesimal transformation is defined by the three equations:

$$\left.\begin{aligned}
dx/dt &= u - \omega_3 y + \omega_2 z + cx(ux + vy + wz),\\
dy/dt &= v - \omega_1 z + \omega_3 x + cy(ux + vy + wz),\\
dz/dt &= w - \omega_2 x + \omega_1 y + cz(ux + vy + wz).
\end{aligned}\right\} \quad \text{(A)}$$

In the case considered in theorem 1 (β), with the proper choice of co-ordinates the three equations defining the general infinitesimal transformations are:

$$\left.\begin{array}{l} dx/dt = u - \omega_3 y + \omega_2 z, \\ dy/dt = v - \omega_1 z + \omega_3 x, \\ dz/dt = w - \omega_2 x + \omega_1 y. \end{array}\right\} \quad \text{(B)}$$

In this case the latent plane is the plane for which at least one of x, y, z are infinite, that is, the plane $0.x + 0.y + 0.z + a = 0$; and the latent conic is the conic in which the cone $x^2 + y^2 + z^2 = 0$ intersects the latent plane.

It follows from theorems 1 and 2 that there is not one unique congruence group, but an indefinite number of them. There is one congruence-group corresponding to each closed real quadric, one to each imaginary quadric with a real equation, and one to each imaginary conic in a real plane and with a real equation. The quadric thus associated with each congruence-group is called the *absolute* for that group, and in the degenerate case of 1 (β) the absolute is the latent plane together with the latent imaginary conic. If the absolute is real, the congruence-group is *hyperbolic;* if imaginary, it is *elliptic;* if the absolute is a plane and imaginary conic, the group is parabolic. Metrical geometry is simply the theory of the properties of some particular congruence-group selected for study.

The definition of distance is connected with the corresponding congruence-group by two considerations in respect to a range of five points $(A_1, A_2, P_1, P_2, P_3)$, of which A_1 and A_2 are on the absolute.

Let $\{A_1 P_1 A_2 P_2\}$ stand for the cross ratio (as defined above) of the range $(A_1 P_1 A_2 P_2)$, with a similar notation for the other ranges. Then

(1) $\log \{A_1 P_1 A_2 P_2\} + \log \{A_1 P_2 A_2 P_3\} = \log \{A_1 P_1 A_2 P_3\}$, and

(2), if the points A_1, A_2, P_1, P_2 are transformed into A'_1, A'_2, P'_1, P'_2 by any transformation of the congruence-group (α) $\{A_1 P_1 A_2 P_2\} = \{A'_1 P'_1 A'_2 P'_2\}$, since the transformation is projective, and (β) A'_1, A'_2, are on the absolute since A_1 and A_2 are on it. Thus if we define the distance P_1P_2 to be $\frac{1}{2}k \log \{A_1P_1A_2P_2\}$, where A_1 and A_2 are the points in which the line P_1P_2 cuts the absolute, and k is some constant, the two characteristic properties of distance, namely, (1) the addition of consecutive lengths on a straight line, and (2) the invariability of distances during a transformation of the congruence-group, are satisfied. This is the well-known Cayley-Klein projective definition[29] of distance, which was elaborated in view of the addition property alone, previously to Lie's discovery of the theory of congruence-groups. For a hyperbolic group when P_1 and P_2 are in the region enclosed by the absolute, $\log \{A_1P_1A_2P_2\}$ is real, and therefore k must be real. For an elliptic group A_1 and A_2 are conjugate imaginaries, and $\log \{A_1P_1A_2P_2\}$ is a pure imaginary, and k is chosen to be $\varkappa/\iota$, where $\varkappa$ is real and $\iota = \sqrt{-}$.

Similarly the angle between two planes, p_1 and p_2, is defined to be $(1/2\iota) \log (t_1p_1t_2p_2)$, where t_1 and t_2 are tangent planes to the absolute through the line p_1p_2. The planes t_1 and t_2 are imaginary for an elliptic group, and also for an hyperbolic group when the planes p_1 and p_2 intersect at points within the region enclosed by the absolute. The development of the consequences of these metrical definitions is the subject of non-Euclidean geometry.

The definitions for the parabolic case can be arrived at as limits of those obtained in either of the other two cases by making k ultimately to vanish. It is also obvious that, if P_1 and P_2 be the points (x_1,y_1,z_1) and (x_2,y_2,z_2), it follows from equations (B) above that $\{(x_1 - x_2)^2 + (y_1 - y_2)^2 + (z_1 - z_2)^2\}^{\frac{1}{2}}$ is unaltered by a congruence transformation and also satisfies the addition property for collinear distances. Also the previous definition of an angle can be adapted to this case, by making t_1 and t_2 to be the tangent planes through the line p_1p_2 to the imaginary conic. Similarly if p_1 and p_2 are inter-

[29] Cf. A. Cayley, "A Sixth Memoir on Quantics," *Trans. Roy. Soc.*, 1859, and *Coll. Papers*, vol. ii; and F. Klein, *Math. Ann.* vol. iv, 1871.

secting lines, the same definition of an angle holds, where t_1 and t_2 are now the lines from the point p_1p_2 to the two points where the plane p_1p_2 cuts the imaginary conic. These points are in fact the "circular points at infinity" on the plane. The development of the consequences of these definitions for the parabolic case gives the ordinary Euclidean metrical geometry.

Thus the only metrical geometry for the whole of projective space is of the elliptic type. But the actual measure-relations (though not their general properties) differ according to the elliptic congruence-group selected for study. In a descriptive space a congruence-group should possess the four characteristics of such a group throughout the whole of the space. Then form the associated ideal projective space. The associated congruence-group for this ideal space must satisfy the four conditions throughout the region of the proper ideal points. Thus the boundary of this region is the absolute. Accordingly there can be no metrical geometry for the whole of a descriptive space unless its boundary (in the associated ideal space) is a closed quadric or a plane. If the boundary is a closed quadric, there is one possible congruence-group of the hyperbolic type. If the boundary is a plane (the plane at infinity), the possible congruence-groups are parabolic; and there is a congruence-group corresponding to each imaginary conic in this plane, together with a Euclidean metrical geometry corresponding to each such group. Owing to these alternative possibilities, it would appear to be more accurate to say that systems of quantities can be found in a space, rather than that space is a quantity.

Lie has also deduced[30] the same results with respect to congruence-groups from another set of defining properties, which explicitly assume the existence of a quantitative relation (the distance) between any two points, which is invariant for any transformation of the congruence-group.[31]

[30] Cf. *loc. cit.*

[31] For similar deductions from a third set of axioms, suggested in essence by Peano, *Riv. mat.*, vol. iv, *loc. cit.*, cf. Whitehead, *Desc. Geom.*, *loc. cit.*

The above results, in respect to congruence and metrical geometry, considered in relation to existent space, have led to the doctrine[32] that it is intrinsically unmeaning to ask which system of metrical geometry is true of the physical world. Any one of these systems can be applied, and in an indefinite number of ways. The only question before us is one of convenience in respect to simplicity of statement of the physical laws. This point of view seems to neglect the consideration that science is to be relevant to the definite perceiving minds of men; and that (neglecting the ambiguity introduced by the invariable slight inexactness of observation which is not relevant to this special doctrine) we have, in fact, presented to our senses a definite set of transformations forming a congruence-group, resulting in a set of measure relations which are in no respect arbitrary. Accordingly our scientific laws are to be stated relevantly to that particular congruence-group. Thus the investigation of the type (elliptic, hyperbolic or parabolic) of this special congruence-group is a perfectly definite problem, to be decided by experiment. The consideration of experiments adapted to this object requires some development of non-Euclidean geometry (see section VI, *Non-Euclidean Geometry*). But if the doctrine means that, assuming some sort of objective reality for the material universe, beings can be imagined, to whom *either* all congruence-groups are equally important, *or* some other congruence-group is specially important, the doctrine appears to be an immediate deduction from the mathematical facts. Assuming a definite congruence-group, the investigation of surfaces (or three-dimensional loci in space of four dimensions) with geodesic geometries of the form of metrical geometries of other types of congruence-groups forms an important chapter of non-Euclidean geometry. Arising from this investigation there is a widely-spread fallacy, which has found its way into many philosophic writings, namely, that the possibility of the geometry of existent three-dimensional space being other than Euclidean depends on the physical

[33] Cf. H. Poincaré, *La Science et l'hypothèse,* ch. iii.

existence of Euclidean space of four or more dimensions. The foregoing exposition shows the baselessness of this idea.

BIBLIOGRAPHY.—For an account of the investigations on the axioms of geometry during the Greek period, see M. Cantor, *Vorlesungen über die Geschichte der Mathematik;* Bd. i and iii; T. L. Heath, *The Thirteen Books of Euclid's Elements, a New Translation from the Greek, with Introductory Essays and Commentary, Historical, Critical and Explanatory* (Cambridge, 1908)— this work is the standard source of information; W. B. Frankland, *Euclid, Book I, with a Commentary* (Cambridge. 1905)—the commentary contains copious extracts from the ancient commentators. The next period of really substantive importance is that of the eighteenth century. The leading authors are: G. Saccheri, S.J., *Euclides ab omni naevo vindicatus* (Milan, 1733). Saccheri was an Italian Jesuit who unconsciously discovered non-Euclidean geometry in the course of his efforts to prove its impossibility. J. H. Lambert, *Theorie der Parallellinien* (1766); A. M. Legendre, *Éléments de géométrie* (1794). An adequate account of the above authors is given by P. Stäckel and F. Engel, *Die Theorie der Parallellinien von Euklid bis auf Gauss* (Leipzig, 1895). The next period of time (roughly from 1800 to 1870) contains two streams of thought, both of which are essential to the modern analysis of the subject. The first stream is that which produced the discovery and investigation of non-Euclidean geometries, the second stream is that which has produced the geometry of position, comprising both projective and descriptive geometry not very accurately discriminated. The leading authors on non-Euclidean geometry are K. F. Gauss, in private letters to Schumacher, cf. Stäckel and Engel, *loc. cit.;* N. Lobatchewsky, rector of the university of Kazan, to whom the honour of the effective discovery of non-Euclidean geometry must be assigned. His first publication was at Kazan in 1826. His various memoirs have been re-edited by Engel; cf. *Urkunden zur Geschichte der nichteuklidischen Geometrie* by Stäckel and Engel, vol. i, "Lobatchewsky." J. Bolyai discovered non-Euclidean geometry apparently in independence of Lobatchewsky. His memoir was published in 1831 as an appendix to a work by his father W. Bolyai, *Tentamen juventutem. . . .* This memoir has been separately edited by J. Frischauf, *Absolute Geometrie nach J. Bolyai* (Leipzig, 1872); B. Riemann, *Über die Hypothesen, welche der Geometrie zu Grunde liegen* (1854); cf. *Gesamte Werke*, a translation in *The Collected Papers* of W. K. Clifford. This is a fundamental memoir on the subject and must rank with the work of Lobatchewsky. Riemann discovered elliptic metrical geometry, and Lobatchewsky hyperbolic geometry. A full account of Riemann's ideas, with the subsequent developments due to Clifford, F. Klein and W. Killing, will be found in *The Boston Colloquium for* 1903 (New York, 1905), article "Forms of Non-Euclidean Space," by F. S. Woods. A. Cayley, *loc. cit.* (1859), and F. Klein, "Über die sogenannte nichteuklidische Geometrie," *Math. Annal.* vols. iv and vi (1871 and 1872), between them elaborated the projective theory of distance; H. Helmholtz, "Über die thatsächlichen Grundlagen der Geometrie" (1866), and "Über die Thatsachen, die der Geometrie zu Grunde liegen" (1868), both in his *Wissenschaftliche Abhandlungen,* vol. ii, and S. Lie, *loc. cit.* (1890 and 1893), between them elaborated the group theory of congruence.

The numberless works which have been written to suggest equivalent alternatives to Euclid's parallel axioms may be neglected as being of trivial importance, though many of them are marvels of geometric ingenuity.

The second stream of thought confined itself within the circle of ideas of Euclidean geometry. Its origin was mainly due to a succession of great French mathematicians, for example, G. Monge, *Géométrie descriptive* (1800); J. V. Poncelet, *Traité des propriétés projectives des figures* (1822); M. Chasles, *Aperçu historique sur l'origine et le développement des méthodes en géométrie* (Bruxelles, 1837) and *Traité de géométrie supérieure* (Paris, 1852); and many others. But the works which have been, and are still, of decisive influence on thought as a store-house of ideas relevant to the foundations of geometry are K. G. C. von Staudt's two works, *Geometrie der Lage* (Nürnberg, 1847); and *Beiträge zur Geometrie der Lage* (Nürnberg, 1856, 3rd ed. 1860).

The final period is characterized by the successful production of exact systems of axioms, and by the final solution of problems which have occupied mathematicians for two thousand years. The successful analysis of the ideas involved in serial continuity is due to R. Dedekind, *Stetigkeit und irrationale Zahlen* (1872), and to G. Cantor, *Grundlagen einer allgemeinen Mannigfaltigkeitslehre* (Leipzig, 1883), and *Acta math.* vol. 2.

Complete systems of axioms have been stated by M. Pasch, *loc. cit.;* G. Peano, *loc. cit.;* M. Pieri, *loc. cit.;* B. Russell, *Principles of Mathematics;* O. Veblen, *loc. cit.;* and by G. Veronese in his treatise, *Fondamenti di geometria* (Padua, 1891; German transl. by A. Schepp, *Grundzüge der Geometrie,* Leipzig, 1894). Most of the leading memoirs on special questions involved have been cited in the text; in addition there may be mentioned M. Pieri, "Nuovi principii di geometria projettiva complessa," *Trans. Accad. R. d. Sci.* (Turin, 1905); E. H. Moore, "On the Projective Axioms of Geometry," *Trans. Amer. Math. Soc.,* 1902; O. Veblen and W. H. Bussey, "Finite Projective Geometries," *Trans. Amer. Math. Soc.,* 1905; A. B. Kempe, "On the Relation between the Logical Theory of Classes and the Geometrical Theory of Points," *Proc. Lond. Math. Soc.,* 1890; J. Royce, "The Relation of the Principles of Logic to the Foundations of Geometry," *Trans. of Amer. Math. Soc.,* 1905; A. Schoenflies, "Über die Möglichkeit einer projectiven Geometrie bei transfiniter (nichtarchimedischer) Massbestimmung," *Deutsch. M.-V. Jahresb.,* 1906.

For general expositions of the bearings of the above investigations, cf. Hon. Bertrand Russell, *loc. cit.;* L. Couturat, *Les Principes des mathématiques* (Paris, 1905); H. Poincaré, *loc. cit.;* Russell and Whitehead, *Principia mathematica* (Cambridge Univ. Press). The philosophers whose views on space and geometric truth deserve especial study are Descartes, Leibniz, Hume, Kant and J. S. Mill. (A. N. W.)

Mathematics

MATHEMATICS (Gr. μαξηματική, *sc.* τέχνη or ἐπιστήμη; from μάξημα, "learning" or "science"), the general term for the various applications of mathematical thought, the traditional field of which is number and quantity. It has been usual to define mathematics as "the science of discrete and continuous magnitude." Even Leibniz,[1] who initiated a more modern point of view, follows the tradition in thus confining the scope of mathematics properly so called, while apparently conceiving it as a department of a yet wider science of reasoning. A short consideration of some leading topics of the science will exemplify both the plausibility and inadequacy of the above definition. Arithmetic, algebra, and the infinitesimal calculus are sciences directly concerned with integral numbers, rational (or fractional) numbers, and real numbers generally, which include incommensurable numbers. It would seem that "the general theory of discrete and continuous quantity" is the exact description of the topics of these sciences. Furthermore, can we not complete the circle of the mathematical sciences by adding geometry? Now geometry deals with points, lines, planes and cubic contents. Of these all except points are quantities: lines involve lengths, planes involve areas, and cubic contents involve volumes. Also, as the Cartesian geometry shows, all the relations between points are expressible in terms of geometric quantities. Ac-

[1] Cf. *La Logique de Leibniz,* ch. vii, by L. Couturat (Paris, 1901).

cordingly, at first sight it seems reasonable to define geometry in some such way as "the science of dimensional quantity." Thus every subdivision of mathematical science would appear to deal with quantity, and the definition of mathematics as "the science of quantity" would appear to be justified. We have now to consider the reasons for rejecting this definition as inadequate.

Types of Critical Questions.—What are numbers? We can talk of five apples and ten pears. But what are "five" and "ten" apart from the apples and pears? Also in addition to the cardinal numbers there are the ordinal numbers: the fifth apple and the tenth pear claim thought. What is the relation of "the fifth" and "the tenth" to "five" and "ten"? "The first rose of summer" and "the last rose of summer" are parallel phrases, yet one explicitly introduces an ordinal number and the other does not. Again, "half a foot" and "half a pound" are easily defined. But in what sense is there "a half," which is the same for "half a foot" as "half a pound"? Furthermore, incommensurable numbers are defined as the limits arrived at as the result of certain procedures with rational numbers. But how do we know that there is anything to reach? We must know that $\sqrt{2}$ exists before we can prove that any procedure will reach it. An expedition to the North Pole has nothing to reach unless the earth rotates.

Also in geometry, what is a point? The straightness of a straight line and the planeness of a plane require consideration. Furthermore, "congruence" is a difficulty. For when a triangle "moves," the points do not move with it. So what is it that keeps unaltered in the moving triangle? Thus the whole method of measurement in geometry as described in the elementary textbooks and the older treatises is obscure to the last degree. Lastly, what are "dimensions"? All these topics require thorough discussion before we can rest content with the definition of mathematics as the general science of magnitude; and by the time they are discussed the definition has evaporated. An outline of the modern answers to questions such as the above will now be given. A critical defence of them would require a volume.[2]

Cardinal Numbers.—A one-one relation between the members of two classes α and β is any method of correlating all the members of α to all the members of β, so that any member of α has one and only one correlate in β, and any member of β has one and only one correlate in α. Two classes between which a one-one relation exists have the same cardinal number and are called cardinally similar; and the cardinal number of the class α is a certain class whose members are themselves classes —namely, it is the class composed of all those classes for which a one-one correlation with α exists. Thus the cardinal number of α is itself a class, and furthermore α is a member of it. For a one-one relation can be established between the members of α and α by the simple process of correlating each member of α with itself. Thus the cardinal number one is the class of unit classes, the cardinal number two is the class of doublets, and so on. Also a unit class is any class with the property that it possesses a member x such that, if y is any member of the class, then x and y are identical. A doublet is any class which possesses a member x such that the modified class formed by all the other members except x is a unit class. And so on for all the finite cardinals, which are thus defined successively. The cardinal number zero is the class of classes with no members; but there is only one such class, namely—the null class. Thus this cardinal number has only one member. The operations of addition and multiplication of two given cardinal numbers can be defined by taking two classes α and β, satisfying the conditions (1) that their cardinal numbers are respectively the given numbers, and (2) that they contain no member in common, and then by defining by reference to α and β two other suitable classes whose cardinal numbers are defined to be respectively the required sum and product of the cardinal numbers in question. We need not here consider the details of this process.

[2] Cf. *The Principles of Mathematics*, by Bertrand Russell (Cambridge, 1903).

With these definitions it is now possible to *prove* the following six premises applying to finite cardinal numbers, from which Peano[8] has shown that all arithmetic can be deduced:—

i. Cardinal numbers form a class.

ii. Zero is a cardinal number.

iii. If a is a cardinal number, $a + 1$ is a cardinal number.

iv. If s is any class and zero is a member of it, also if when x is a cardinal number and a member of s, also $x + 1$ is a member of s, then the whole class of cardinal numbers is contained in s.

v. If a and b are cardinal numbers, and $a + 1 = b + 1$, then $a = b$.

vi. If a is a cardinal number, then $a + 1 \neq 0$.

It may be noticed that (iv) is the familiar principle of mathematical induction. Peano in an historical note refers its first explicit employment, although without a general enunciation, to Maurolycus in his work, *Arithmeticorum libri duo* (Venice, 1575).

But now the difficulty of confining mathematics to being the science of number and quantity is immediately apparent. For there is no self-contained science of cardinal numbers. The proof of the six premises requires an elaborate investigation into the general properties of classes and relations which can be deduced by the strictest reasoning from our ultimate logical principles. Also it is purely arbitrary to erect the consequences of these six principles into a separate science. They are excellent principles of the highest value, but they are in no sense the necessary premises which must be proved before any other propositions of cardinal numbers can be established. On the contrary, the premises of arithmetic can be put in other forms, and, furthermore, an indefinite number of propositions of arithmetic can be proved directly from logical principles without men-

[8] Cf. *Formulaire mathématique* (Turin, ed. of 1903); earlier formulations of the bases of arithmetic are given by him in the editions of 1898 and of 1901. The variations are only trivial.

tioning them. Thus, while arithmetic may be defined as that branch of deductive reasoning concerning classes and relations which is concerned with the establishment of propositions concerning cardinal numbers, it must be added that the introduction of cardinal numbers makes no great break in this general science. It is no more than an interesting subdivision in a general theory.

Ordinal Numbers.—We must first understand what is meant by "order," that is, by "serial arrangement." An order of a set of things is to be sought in that relation holding between members of the set which constitutes that order. The set viewed as a class has many orders. Thus the telegraph posts along a certain road have a space-order very obvious to our senses; but they have also a time-order according to dates of erection, perhaps more important to the postal authorities who replace them after fixed intervals. A set of cardinal numbers have an order of magnitude, often called *the* order of the set because of its insistent obviousness to us; but, if they are the numbers drawn in a lottery, their time-order of occurrence in that drawing also ranges them in an order of some importance. Thus the order is defined by the "serial" relation. A relation (R) is serial[4] when (1) it implies diversity, so that, if x has the relation R to y, x is diverse from y; (2) it is transitive, so that if x has the relation R to y, and y to z, then x has the relation R to z; (3) it has the property of connexity, so that if x and y are things to which any things bear the relation R, or which bear the relation R to any things, then *either* x is identical with y, *or* x has the relation R to y, *or* y has the relation R to x. These conditions are necessary and sufficient to secure that our ordinary ideas of "preceding" and "succeeding" hold in respect to the relation R. The "field" of relation R is the class of things ranged in order by it. Two relations R and R' are said to be ordinally similar, if a one-one relation holds between the members of the two fields of R and R', such that if x and y are any two members of the field of R, such that x has the relation R to y, and if x' and y' are

[4] Cf. Russell, *loc. cit.*, pp. 199-256.

the correlates in the field of R' of x and y, then in all such cases x' has the relation R' to y', and conversely, interchanging the dashes on the letters, i.e. R and R', x and x', etcetera. It is evident that the ordinal similarity of two relations implies the cardinal similarity of their fields, but not conversely. Also, two relations need not be serial in order to be ordinally similar; but if one is serial, so is the other. The relation-number of a relation is the class whose members are all those relations which are ordinally similar to it. This class will include the original relation itself. The relation-number of a relation should be compared with the cardinal number of a class. When a relation is serial its relation-number is often called its serial type. The addition and multiplication of two relation-numbers is defined by taking two relations R and S, such that (1) their fields have no terms in common; (2) their relation-numbers are the two relation-numbers in question, and then by defining by reference to R and S two other suitable relations whose relation-numbers are defined to be respectively the sum and product of the relation-numbers in question. We need not consider the details of this process. Now if n be any finite cardinal number, it can be proved that the class of those serial relations, which have a field whose cardinal number is n, is a relation-number. This relation-number is the ordinal number corresponding to n; let it be symbolized by $\dot{n}$. Thus, corresponding to the cardinal numbers 2, 3, 4 . . . there are the ordinal numbers $\dot{2}$, $\dot{3}$, $\dot{4}$ . . . The definition of the ordinal number $\dot{1}$ requires some little ingenuity owing to the fact that no serial relation can have a field whose cardinal number is 1; but we must omit here the explanation of the process. The ordinal number 0 is the class whose sole member is the null relation—that is, the relation which never holds between any pair of entities. The definitions of the finite ordinals can be expressed without use of the corresponding cardinals, so there is no essential priority of cardinals to ordinals. Here also it can be seen that the science of the finite ordinals is a particular subdivision of the general theory of classes and relations. Thus the illusory nature of the traditional definition of mathematics is again illustrated.

Cantor's Infinite Numbers.—Owing to the correspondence between the finite cardinals and the finite ordinals, the propositions of cardinal arithmetic and ordinal arithmetic correspond point by point. But the definition of the cardinal number of a class applies when the class is not finite, and it can be proved that there are different infinite cardinal numbers, and that there is a least infinite cardinal, now usually denoted by $\aleph_0$, where $\aleph$ is the Hebrew letter aleph. Similarly, a class of serial relations, called *well-ordered* serial relations, can be defined, such that their corresponding relation-numbers include the ordinary finite ordinals, but also include relation-numbers which have many properties like those of the finite ordinals, though the fields of the relations belonging to them are not finite. These relation-numbers are the infinite ordinal numbers. The arithmetic of the infinite cardinals does not correspond to that of the infinite ordinals. The theory of these extensions of the ideas of number is dealt with in the article. It will suffice to mention here that Peano's fourth premiss of arithmetic does not hold for infinite cardinals or for infinite ordinals. Contrasting the above definitions of number, cardinal and ordinals, with the alternative theory that number is an ultimate idea incapable of definition, we notice that our procedure exacts a greater attention combined with a smaller credulity; for every idea, assumed as ultimate, demands a separate act of faith.

The Data of Analysis.—Rational numbers and real numbers in general can now be defined according to the same general method. If m and n are finite cardinal numbers, the rational number m/n is the relation which any finite cardinal number x bears to any finite cardinal number y when $n \times x = m \times y$. Thus the rational number one, which we will denote by 1_r, is not the cardinal number 1; for 1_r is the relation 1/1 as defined above, and is thus a relation holding between certain pairs of cardinals. Similarly, the other rational integers must be distinguished from the corresponding cardinals. The arithmetic of rational numbers is now established by means of appropriate definitions, which indicate the entities meant by the operations of addition and multiplication. But the desire to obtain general enunciations of theorems without exceptional cases has led mathematicians to employ entities of ever-ascending types of elaboration. These entities are not created by mathematicians, they are employed by them, and their definitions should point out the construction of the new entities in terms of those already on hand. The real numbers, which include irrational numbers, have now to be defined. Consider the serial arrangement of the rationals in their order of magnitude. A real number is a class (α, say) of rational numbers which satisfies the condition that it is the same as the class of those rationals each of which precedes at least one member of α. Thus, consider the class of rationals less than 2_r; any member of this class precedes some other members of the class—thus $1/2$ precedes $4/3$, $3/2$ and so on; also the class of predecessors of predecessors of 2_r is itself the class of predecessors of 2_r. Accordingly this class is a real number; it will be called the real number 2_R. Note that the class of rationals less than or equal to 2_r is not a real number. For 2_r is not a predecessor of some member of the class. In the above example 2_R is an integral real number, which is distinct from a rational integer, and from a cardinal number. Similarly, any rational real number is distinct from the corresponding rational number. But now the irrational real numbers have all made their appearance. For example, the class of rationals whose squares are less than 2_r satisfies the definition of a real number; it is the real number $\sqrt{2}$. The arithmetic of real numbers follows from appropriate definitions of the operations of addition and multiplication. Except for the immediate purposes of an explanation, such as the above, it is unnecessary for mathematicians to have separate symbols, such as 2, 2_r and 2_R, or $2/3$ and $(2/3)_R$. Real numbers with signs ($+$ or $-$) are now defined. If a is a real number, $+a$ is defined to be the relation which any real number of the form $x + a$ bears to the real number x,

104

and $-a$ is the relation which any real number x bears to the real number $x + a$. The addition and multiplication of these "signed" real numbers is suitably defined, and it is proved that the usual arithmetic of such numbers follows. Finally, we reach a complex number of the nth order. Such a number is a "one-many" relation which relates n signed real numbers (or n algebraic complex numbers when they are already defined by this procedure) to the n cardinal numbers 1, 2 . . . n respectively. If such a complex number is written (as usual) in the form $x_1e_1 + x_2e_2 + \ldots + x_ne_n$, then this particular complex number relates x_1 to 1, x_2 to 2, . . . x_1 to n. Also the "unit" e_1 (or e_s) considered as a number of the system is merely a shortened form for the complex number $(+1)$ $e_1 + 0e_2 + \ldots + 0e_n$. This last number exemplifies the fact that one signed real number, such as 0, may be correlated to many of the n cardinals, such as 2 . . . n in the example, but that each cardinal is only correlated with one signed number. Hence the relation has been called above "one-many." The sum of two complex numbers $x_1e_1 + x_2e_2 + \ldots + x_ne_n$ and $y_1e_1 + y_2e_2 + \ldots y_ne_n$ is always defined to be the complex number $(x_1 + y_1)e_1 + (x_2 + y_2)e_2 + \ldots + (x_n + y_n)e_n$. But an indefinite number of definitions of the product of two complex numbers yield interesting results. Each definition gives rise to a corresponding algebra of higher complex numbers. We will confine ourselves here to algebraic complex numbers—that is, to complex numbers of the second order taken in connexion with that definition of multiplication which leads to ordinary algebra. The product of two complex numbers of the second order—namely, $x_1e_1 + x_2e_2$ and $y_1e_1 + y_2e_2$, is in this case defined to mean the complex $(x_1y_1 - x_2y_2)e_1 + (x_1y_2 + x_2y_1)e_2$. Thus $e_1 \times e_1 = e_1$, $e_2 \times e_2 = -e_1$, $e_1 \times e_2 = e_2 \times e_1 = e_2$. With this definition it is usual to omit the first symbol e_1, and to write i or $\sqrt{-1}$ instead of e_2. Accordingly, the typical form for such a complex number is $x + yi$, and then with this notation the above-mentioned definition of multiplication is invariably adopted. The importance of this algebra arises from the fact that in terms of such complex numbers with this definition of multiplication the utmost generality of expression, to the exclusion of exceptional cases, can be obtained for theorems which occur in analogous forms, but complicated with exceptional cases in the algebras of real numbers and of signed real numbers. This is exactly the same reason as that which has led mathematicians to work with signed real numbers in preference to real numbers, and with real numbers in preference to rational numbers. The evolution of mathematical thought in the invention of the data of analysis has thus been completely traced in outline.

Definition of Mathematics.—It has now become apparent that the traditional field of mathematics in the province of discrete and continuous number can only be separated from the general abstract theory of classes and relations by a wavering and indeterminate line. Of course a discussion as to the mere application of a word easily degenerates into the most fruitless logomachy. It is open to any one to use any word in any sense. But on the assumption that "mathematics" is to denote a science well marked out by its subject matter and its methods from other topics of thought, and that at least it is to include all topics habitually assigned to it, there is now no option but to employ "mathematics" in the general sense[5] of the "science concerned with the logical deduction of consequences from the general premisses of all reasoning."

Geometry.—The typical mathematical proposition is: "If x, y, z . . . satisfy such and such conditions, then such and such other conditions hold with respect to them." By taking fixed conditions for the hypothesis of

[5] The first unqualified explicit statement of *part* of this definition seems to be by B. Peirce, "Mathematics is the science which draws necessary conclusions," *Linear Associative Algebra*, § i (1870), republished in the *Amer. Journ. of Math.*, vol. iv (1881). But it will be noticed that the second half of the definition in the text— "from the general premisses of all reasoning"—is left unexpressed. The full expression of the idea and its development into a philosophy of mathematics is due to Russell, *loc. cit.*

such a proposition a definite department of mathematics is marked out. For example, geometry is such a department. The "axioms" of geometry are the fixed conditions which occur in the hypotheses of the geometrical propositions. The special nature of the "axioms" which constitute geometry is considered in the article GEOMETRY (*Axioms*). It is sufficient to observe here that they are concerned with special types of classes of classes and of classes of relations, and that the connexion of geometry with number and magnitude is in no way an essential part of the foundation of the science. In fact, the whole theory of measurement in geometry arises at a comparatively late stage as the result of a variety of complicated considerations.

Classes and Relations.—The foregoing account of the nature of mathematics necessitates a strict deduction of the general properties of classes and relations from the ultimate logical premises. In the course of this process, undertaken for the first time with the rigour of mathematicians, some contradictions have become apparent. That first discovered is known as Burali-Forti's contradiction,[6] and consists in the proof that there both is and is not a greatest infinite ordinal number. But these contradictions do not depend upon any theory of number, for Russell's contradiction[7] does not involve number in any form. This contradiction arises from considering the class possessing as members all classes which are not members of themselves. Call this class w; then to say that x is a w is equivalent to saying that x is not an x. Accordingly, to say that w is a w is equivalent to saying that w is not a w. An analogous contradiction can be found for relations. It follows that a careful scrutiny of the very idea of classes and relations is required. Note that classes are here required in extension, so that the class of human beings and the class of rational featherless bipeds are identical; similarly for relations, which

[6] "Una questione sui numeri transfiniti," *Rend. del circolo mat. di Palermo*, vol. xi (1897) ; and Russell, *loc. cit.*, ch. xxxviii.
[7] Cf. Russell, *loc. cit.*, ch. x.

are to be determined by the entities related. Now a class in respect to its components is many. In what sense then can it be one? This problem of "the one and the many" has been discussed continuously by the philosophers.[8] All the contradictions can be avoided, and yet the use of classes and relations can be preserved as required by mathematics, and indeed by common sense, by a theory which denies to a class—or relation—existence or being in any sense in which the entities composing it—or related by it—exist. Thus, to say that a pen is an entity and the class of pens is an entity is merely a play upon the word "entity"; the second sense of "entity" (if any) is indeed derived from the first, but has a more complex signification. Consider an incomplete proposition, incomplete in the sense that some entity which ought to be involved in it is represented by an undetermined x, which may stand for any entity. Call it a propositional function; and, if φx be a propositional function, the undetermined variable x is the argument. Two propositional functions φx and ψx are "extensionally identical" if any determination of x in φx which converts φx into a true proposition also converts ψx into a true proposition, and conversely for ψ and φ. Now consider a propositional function $F\chi$ in which the variable argument χ is itself a propositional function. If $F\chi$ is true when, and only when, χ is determined to be either φ or some other propositional function extensionally equivalent to φ, then the proposition $F\varphi$ is of the form which is ordinarily recognized as being about the class determined by φx taken in extension—that is, the class of entities for which φx is a true proposition when x is determined to be any one of them. A similar theory holds for relations which arise from the consideration of propositional functions with two or more variable arguments. It is then possible to define by a parallel elaboration what is meant by class of classes, classes of relations, relations between classes, and so on. Accordingly, the number of a class of relations can be defined, or of a class of classes, and so

[8] Cf. *Pragmatism: a New Name for some Old Ways of Thinking* (1907).

on. This theory[9] is in effect a theory of the use of classes and relations, and does not decide the philosophic question as to the sense (if any) in which a class in extension is one entity. It does indeed deny that it is an entity in the sense in which one of its members is an entity. Accordingly, it is fallacy for any determination of x to consider "x is an x" or "x is not an x" as having the meaning of propositions. Note that for any determination of x, "x is an x" and "x is not an x" are neither of them fallacies but are both meaningless, according to this theory. Thus Russell's contradiction vanishes, and an examination of the other contradictions shows that they vanish also.

Applied Mathematics.—The selection of the topics of mathematical inquiry among the infinite variety open to it has been guided by the useful applications, and indeed the abstract theory has only recently been disentangled from the empirical elements connected with these applications. For example, the application of the theory of cardinal numbers to classes of physical entities involves in practice some process of counting. It is only recently that the *succession* of processes which is involved in any act of counting has been seen to be irrelevant to the idea of number. Indeed, it is only by experience that we can know that any definite process of counting will give the true cardinal number of some class of entities. It is perfectly possible to imagine a universe in which any act of counting by a being in it annihilated some members of the class counted during the time and only during the time of its continuance. A legend of the Council of Nicea[10] illustrates this point: "When the Bishops took their places on their thrones they were 318; when they rose up to be called over, it appeared that they were 319; so that they never could make the

---

[9] Due to Bertrand Russell, cf. "Mathematical Logic as based on the Theory of Types," *Amer. Journ. of Math.*, vol. xxx (1908). It is more fully explained by him, with later simplifications, in *Principia mathematica* (Cambridge).

[10] Cf. Stanley's *Eastern Church*, Lecture v.

number come right, and whenever they approached the last of the series, he immediately turned into the likeness of his next neighbour." Whatever be the historical worth of this story, it may safely be said that it cannot be disproved by deductive reasoning from the premisses of abstract logic. The most we can do is to assert that a universe in which such things are liable to happen on a large scale is unfitted for the practical application of the theory of cardinal numbers. The application of the theory of real numbers to physical quantities involves analogous considerations. In the first place, some physical process of addition is presupposed, involving some inductively inferred law of permanence during that process. Thus in the theory of masses we must know that two pounds of lead when put together will counterbalance in the scales two pounds of sugar, or a pound of lead and a pound of sugar. Furthermore, the sort of continuity of the series (in order of magnitude) of rational numbers is known to be different from that of the series of real numbers. Indeed, mathematicians now reserve "continuity" as the term for the latter kind of continuity; the mere property of having an infinite number of terms between any two terms is called "compactness." The compactness of the series of rational numbers is consistent with quasi-gaps in it—that is, with the possible absence of limits to classes in it. Thus the class of rational numbers whose squares are less than 2 has no upper limit among the rational numbers. But among the real numbers all classes have limits. Now, owing to the necessary in exactness of measurement, it is impossible to discriminate directly whether any kind of continuous physical quantity possesses the compactness of the series of rationals or the continuity of the series of real numbers. In calculations the latter hypothesis is made because of its mathematical simplicity. But, the assumption has certainly no *a priori* grounds in its favour, and it is not very easy to see how to base it upon experience. For example, if it should turn out that the mass of a body is to be estimated by counting the number of corpuscles (whatever they may be) which go to form it, then a body

110

with an irrational measure of mass is intrinsically impossible. Similarly, the continuity of space apparently rests upon sheer assumption unsupported by any *a priori* or experimental grounds. Thus the current applications of mathematics to the analysis of phenomena can be justified by no *a priori* necessity.

In one sense there is no science of applied mathematics. When once the fixed conditions which any hypothetical group of entities are to satisfy have been precisely formulated, the deduction of the further propositions, which also will hold respecting them, can proceed in complete independence of the question as to whether or no any such group of entities can be found in the world of phenomena. Thus rational mechanics, based on the Newtonian Laws, viewed as mathematics is independent of its supposed application, and hydrodynamics remains a coherent and respected science though it is extremely improbable that any perfect fluid exists in the physical world. But this unbendingly logical point of view cannot be the last word upon the matter. For no one can doubt the essential difference between characteristic treatises upon "pure" and "applied" mathematics. The difference is a difference in method. In pure mathematics the hypotheses which a set of entities are to satisfy are given, and a group of interesting deductions are sought. In "applied mathematics" the "deductions" are given in the shape of the experimental evidence of natural science, and the hypotheses from which the "deductions" can be deduced are sought. Accordingly, every treatise on applied mathematics, properly so-called, is directed to the criticism of the "laws" from which the reasoning starts, or to a suggestion of results which experiment may hope to find. Thus if it calculates the result of some experiment, it is not the experimentalist's well-attested results which are on their trial, but the basis of the calculation. Newton's *Hypotheses non fingo* was a proud boast, but it rests upon an entire misconception of the capacities of the mind of man in dealing with external nature.

Synopsis of Existing Developments of Pure Mathematics.—A complete classification of mathematical sciences, as they at present exist, is to be found in the *International Catalogue of Scientific Literature* promoted by the Royal Society. The classification in question was drawn up by an international committee of eminent mathematicians, and thus has the highest authority. It would be unfair to criticize it from an exacting philosophical point of view. The practical object of the enterprise required that the proportionate quantity of yearly output in the various branches, and that the liability of various topics as a matter of fact to occur in connexion with each other, should modify the classification.

Section A deals with pure mathematics. Under the general heading *"Fundamental Notions"* occur the sub-headings *"Foundations of Arithmetic,"* with the topics rational, irrational and transcendental numbers, and aggregates; *"Universal Algebra,"* with the topics complex numbers, quarternions, ausdehnungslehre, vector analysis, matrices, and algebra of logic; and *"Theory of Groups,"* with the topics finite and continuous groups. Under the general heading *"Algebra and Theory of Numbers"* occur the sub-headings *"Elements of Algebra,"* with the topics rational polynomials, permutations, etcetera, partitions, probabilities; *"Linear Substitutions,"* with the topics determinants, etcetera, linear substitutions, general theory of quantics; *"Theory of Algebraic Equations,"* with the topics existence of roots, separation of and approximation to, theory of Galois, etcetera; *"Theory of Numbers,"* with the topics congruences, quadratic residues, prime numbers, particular irrational and transcendental numbers.

Under the general heading *"Analysis"* occur the sub-headings *"Foundations of Analysis,"* with the topics theory of functions of real variables, series and other infinite processes, principles and elements of the differential and of the integral calculus, definite integrals, and calculus of variations; *"Theory of Functions of Complex Variables,"* with the topics functions of one variable and of several variables; *"Algebraic Functions and their Integrals,"* with the topics algebraic functions of one and of several variables, elliptic functions and single theta functions, Abelian integrals; *"Other Special Functions,"* with the topics Euler's, Legendre's, Bessel's and automorphic functions; *"Differential Equations,"* with the topics existence theorems, methods of solution, general theory; *"Differential Forms and Differential Invariants,"* with the topics differential forms, including Pfaffians, transformation of differential forms, including tangential (or contact) transformations, differential invariants; *"Analytical Methods connected with Physical Subjects,"* with the topics harmonic analysis, Fourier's series, the differential equations of applied mathematics, Dirichlet's problem; *"Difference Equations and Functional Equations,"* with the topics recurring series, solution of equations of finite differences and functional equations. Under the general heading *"Geometry"* occur the sub-headings *"Foundations,"* with the topics principles of geometry, non-Euclidean geometries, hyperspace, methods of analytical geometry; *"Elementary Geometry,"* with the topics planimetry, stereometry, trigonometry, descriptive geometry; *"Geometry of Conics and Quadrics,"* with the implied topics; *"Algebraic Curves and Surfaces of Degree higher than the Second,"* with the implied topics; *"Transformations and General Methods for Algebraic Configurations,"* with the topics collineation, duality, transformations, correspondence, groups of points on algebraic curves and surfaces, genus of curves and surfaces, enumerative geometry, connexes, complexes, congruences, higher elements in space, algebraic configurations in hyperspace; *"Infinitesimal Geometry: applications of Differential and Integral Calculus to Geometry,"* with the topics kinematic geometry, curvature, rectification and quadrature, special transcendental curves and surfaces; *"Differential Geometry: applications of Differential Equations to Geometry,"* with the topics curves on surfaces, minimal surfaces, surfaces determined by differential properties, conformal and other representation of surfaces on others, deformation of surfaces, orthogonal and isothermic surfaces.

This survey of the existing developments of pure mathematics confirms the conclusions arrived at from the previous survey of the theoretical principles of the subject. Functions, operations, transformations, substitutions, correspondences, are but names for various types of relations. A group is a class of relations possessing a special property. Thus the modern ideas, which have so powerfully extended and unified the subject, have loosened its connexion with "number" and "quantity," while bringing ideas of form and structure into increasing prominence. Number must indeed ever remain the great topic of mathematical interest, because it is in reality the great topic of applied mathematics. All the world, including savages who cannot count beyond five, daily "apply" theorems of number. But the complexity of the idea of number is practically illustrated by the fact that it is best studied as a department of a science wider than itself.

Synopsis of Existing Developments of Applied Mathematics.—Section B of the *International Catalogue* deals with mechanics. The heading *"Measurement of Dynamical Quantities"* includes the topics units, measurements, and the constant of gravitation. The topics of the other headings do not require express mention. These headings are: *"Geometry and Kinematics of Particles and Solid Bodies"*; *"Principles of Rational Mechanics"*; *"Statics of Particles, Rigid Bodies, Etcetera"*; *"Kinetics of Particles, Rigid Bodies, Etcetera"*; *General Analytical Mechanics"*; *"Statics and Dynamics of Fluids"*; *"Hydraulics and Fluid Resistances"*; *"Elasticity."* Mechanics (including dynamical astronomy) is that subject among those traditionally classed as "applied" which has been most completely transfused by mathematics—that is to say, which is studied with the deductive spirit of the pure mathematician, and not with the covert inductive intention overlaid with the superficial forms of deduction, characteristic of the applied mathematician.

Every branch of physics gives rise to an application of mathematics. A prophecy may be hazarded that in the future these applications will unify themselves into a mathematical theory of a hypothetical substructure of the universe, uniform under all the diverse phenomena.

The History of Mathematics.—The history of mathematics is in the main history of its various branches. A short account of the history of each branch will be found in connexion with the article which deals with it. Viewing the subject as a whole, and apart from remote developments which have not in fact seriously influenced the great structure of the mathematics of the European races, it may be said to have had its origin with the Greeks, working on pre-existing fragmentary lines of thought derived from the Egyptians and Phœnicians. The Greeks created the sciences of geometry and of number as applied to the measurement of continuous quantities. The great abstract ideas (considered directly and not merely in tacit use) which have dominated the science were due to them—namely, ratio, irrationality, continuity, the point, the straight line, the plane. This period lasted[11] from the time of Thales, c. 600 B.C., to the capture of Alexandria by the Mahomedans, A.D. 641. The mediæval Arabians invented our system of numeration and developed algebra. The next period of advance stretches from the Renaissance to Newton and Leibniz at the end of the seventeenth century. During this period logarithms were invented, trigonometry and algebra developed, analytical geometry invented, dynamics put upon a sound basis, and the period closed with the magnificent invention of (or at least the perfecting of) the differential calculus by Newton and Leibniz and the discovery of gravitation. The eighteenth century witnessed a rapid development of analysis, and the period culminated with the genius of Lagrange and Laplace. This period may be conceived as continuing throughout the first quarter of the nineteenth century. It was remarkable both for the brilliance of its achievements and for the large number of French mathematicians of the first rank who flourished during it. The next period was inaugurated in analysis by K. F. Gauss, N. H. Abel and A. L. Cauchy. Between them the general theory of the complex variable, and of the various "infinite" processes of mathematical analysis, was established, while other mathematicians, such as Poncelet, Steiner, Lobatschewsky and von Staudt, were founding modern geometry, and Gauss inaugurated the differential geometry of surfaces. The applied mathematical sciences of light, electricity and electromagnetism, and of heat,

[11] Cf. *A Short History of Mathematics,* by W. W. R. Ball.

were now largely developed. This school of mathematical thought lasted beyond the middle of the century, after which a change and further development can be traced. In the next and last period the progress of pure mathematics has been dominated by the critical spirit introduced by the German mathematicians under the guidance of Weierstrass, though foreshadowed by earlier analysts, such as Abel. Also such ideas as those of invariants, groups and of form have modified the entire science. But the progress in all directions has been too rapid to admit of any one adequate characterization. During the same period a brilliant group of mathematical physicists, notably Lord Kelvin (W. Thomson), H. V. Helmholtz, J. C. Maxwell, H. Hertz, have transformed applied mathematics by systematically basing their deductions upon the Law of the conservation of energy, and the hypothesis of an ether pervading space.

BIBLIOGRAPHY.—References to the works containing expositions of the various branches of mathematics are given in the appropriate articles. It must suffice here to refer to sources in which the subject is considered as one whole. Most philosophers refer in their works to mathematics more or less cursorily, either in the treatment of the ideas of number and magnitude, or in their consideration of the alleged *a priori* and necessary truths. A bibliography of such references would be in effect a bibliography of metaphysics, or rather of epistemology. The founder of the modern point of view, explained in this article, was Leibniz, who, however, was so far in advance of contemporary thought that his ideas remained neglected and undeveloped until recently; cf. *Opuscules et fragments inédits de Leibnitz. Extraits des manuscrits de la bibliothèque royale de Hanovre,* by Louis Couturat (Paris, 1903), especially pp. 356-399, "Generales inquisitiones de analysi notionum et veritatum" (written in 1686); also cf. *La Logique de Leibnitz,* already referred to. For the modern authors who have rediscovered and improved upon the position of Leibniz, cf. *Grundgesetze der Arithmetik, begriffsschriftlich abgeleitet von Dr. G. Frege, a.o. Professor an der Univ. Jena* (Bd. i, 1893; Bd. ii, 1903, Jena); also cf. Frege's earlier works, *Begriffs-*
116

schrift, eine der arithmetischen nachgebildete Formel-sprache des reinen Denkens (Halle, 1879), and *Die Grundlagen der Arithmetik* (Breslau, 1884); also cf. Bertrand Russell, *The Principles of Mathematics* (Cambridge, 1903), and his article on "Mathematical Logic" in *Amer. Quart. Journ. of Math.* (vol. xxx, 1908). Also the following works are of importance, though not all expressly expounding the Leibnizian point of view: cf. G. Cantor, "Grundlagen einer allgemeinen Mannigfaltig-keits-lehre," *Math. Annal.*, vol. xxi (1883) and subsequent articles in vols. xlvi and xlix; also R. Dedekind, *Stetigkeit und irrationales Zahlen* (ist ed., 1872), and *Was sind und was sollen die Zahlen?* (ist ed., 1887), both tracts translated into English under the title *Essays on the Theory of Numbers* (Chicago, 1901). These works of G. Cantor and Dedekind were of the greatest importance in the progress of the subject. Also cf. G. Peano (with various collaborators of the Italian school), *Formulaire de mathématiques* (Turin, various editions, 1894-1908; the earlier editions are the more interesting philosophically); Felix Klein, *Lectures on Mathematics* (New York, 1894); W. K. Clifford, *The Common Sense of the Exact Sciences* (London, 1885); H. Poincaré, *La Science et l'hypothèse* (Paris, 1st ed., 1902), English translation under the title, *Science and Hypothesis* (London, 1905); L. Couturat, *Les Principes des mathématiques* (Paris, 1905); E. Mach, *Die Mechanik in ihrer Entwickelung* (Prague, 1883), English translation under the title, *The Science of Mechanics* (London, 1893); K. Pearson, *The Grammar of Science* (London, 1st ed., 1892; 2nd ed., 1900, enlarged); A. Cayley, *Presidential Address* (Brit. Assoc., 1883); B. Russell and A. N. Whitehead, *Principia Mathematica* (Cambridge, 1911). For the history of mathematics the one modern and complete source of information is M. Cantor's *Vorlesungen über Geschichte der Mathematik* (Leipzig, 1st Bd., 1880; 2nd Bd., 1892; 3rd Bd., 1898; 4th Bd., 1908; 1st Bd., *von den ältesten Zeiten bis zum Jahre* 1200, *n. Chr.;* 2nd Bd., *von* 1200-1668; 3rd Bd., *von* 1668-1758; 4th Bd., *von* 1795 *bis* 1799); W. W. R. Ball, *A Short History of Mathematics* (London, 1st ed., 1888, three subsequent editions, enlarged and revised, and translations into French and Italian).   (A. N. W.)

Einstein's Theory[1]

EINSTEIN'S WORK MAY be analysed into three factors—a principle, a procedure, and an explanation. This discovery of the principle and the procedure constitute an epoch in science. I venture, however, to think that the explanation is faulty, even although it formed the clue by which Einstein guided himself along the path from his principle to his procedure. It is no novelty to the history of science that factors of thought which guided genius to its goal should be subsequently discarded. The names of Kepler and Maupertuis at once occur in illustration.

What I call Einstein's principle is the connexion between time and space which emerges from his way of envisaging the general fact of relativity. This connexion is entirely new to scientific thought, and is in some respects very paradoxical. A slight sketch of the history of ideas of relative motion will be the shortest way of introducing the new principle. Newton thought that there was one definite space within which the material world adventured, and that the sequence of its adventures could be recorded in terms of one definite time. There would be, therefore, a meaning in asking whether the sun is at rest or is fixed in this space, even although the questioner might be ignorant of the existence of

[1] The articles on this subject, which appeared on January 22 and 29 (1920), summarized the general philosophical theory of the relativity of space and time and the physical ideas involved in Einstein's researches. The purpose of the present article is in some respects critical, with the object of suggesting an alternative explanation of Einstein's great achievement.

other bodies such as the planets and the stars. Furthermore, there was for Newton an absolute unique meaning to simultaneity, so that there can be no ambiguity in asking, without further specification of conditions, which of two events preceded the other or whether they were simultaneous. In other words, Newton held a theory of absolute space and of absolute time. He explained relative motion of one body with respect to another as being the difference of the absolute motions of the two bodies. The greatest enemy to his absolute theory of space was his own set of laws of motion. For it is a well-known result from these laws that it is impossible to detect absolute uniform motion. Accordingly, since we fail to observe variations in the velocities of the sun and stars, it follows that any one of them may with equal right be assumed to be either at rest or moving in any direction with any velocity which we like to suggest. Now, a character which never appears in the play does not require a living actor for its impersonation. Science is concerned with the relations between things perceived. If absolute motion is imperceptible, absolute position is a fairy tale, and absolute space cannot survive the surrender of absolute position.

So far our course is plain: we give up absolute space, and conceive all statements about space as being merely expositions of the internal relations of the physical universe. But we have to take account of two very remarkable difficulties which mar the simplicity of this theoretical position. In the first place there seems to be a certain absoluteness about rotation. The fact of this absoluteness is inherent in Newton's laws of motion, and the deducted consequences from these premises have received ample confirmation. For example, the effect of the rotation of the earth is manifested in phenomena which appear to have no connexion with extraneous astronomical bodies. There is the bulge of the earth at its equator, the invariable directions of rotation for cyclones and anti-cyclones, the rotation of the plane of oscillation of Foucault's pendulum, and the north-seeking property of the gyro-compass. The mass of evidence is decisive, and no theory which burkes it can stand as an adequate explanation of observed facts. It is not so obvious how to combine these facts of rotation with any principle of relativity.

Secondly, the ether contributes another perplexity just where it might have helped us. We might have regained the right quasi-absoluteness of motion by measuring velocity relatively to the ether. The facts of rotation could have thus received an explanation. But all attempts to measure velocity relatively to the ether have failed to detect it in circumstances when, granting the ordinary hypotheses, its effects should have been visible. Einstein showed that the whole series of perplexing facts concerning the ether could be explained by adopting new formulæ connecting the spatial and temporal measurements made by observers in relative motion to each other. These formulæ had been elaborated by Larmor and Lorentz, but it was Einstein who made them the foundation of a novel theory of time and space. He also discovered the remarkable fact that, according to these formulæ, the velocity of light in vacuous space would be identical in magnitude for all these alternative assumptions as to rest or motion. This property of light became the clue by which his researches were guided. His theory of simultaneity is based on the transmission of light signals, and accordingly the whole structure of our concept of nature is essentially bound up with our perceptions of radiant energy.

In view of the magnificent results which Einstein has achieved it may seem rash to doubt the validity of a premiss so essential to his own line of thought. I do, however, disbelieve in this invariant property of the velocity of light, for reasons which have been partly furnished by Einstein's own later researches. The velocity of light appears in this connexion owing to the fact that it occurs in Maxwell's famous equations, which express the laws governing electro-magnetic phenomena. But it is an outcome of Einstein's work that the electromagnetic equations require modification to express the association of the gravitational and electro-magnetic fields. This is one of his greatest discoveries. The most natural deduction to make from these modified equations is that the velocity of light is modified by the gravitational properties of the field through which it passes, and that the absolute maximum velocity which occurs in the Maxwellian form of the equations has in fact a different origin which is independent of any special relation to light or electricity. I will return to this question later.

Before passing on to Einstein's later work a tribute should be paid to the genius of Minkowski. It was he who stated in its full generality the conception of a four-dimensional world embracing space and time, in which the ultimate elements, or points, are the infinitesimal occurrences in the life of each particle. He built on Einstein's foundations, and his work forms an essential factor in the evolution of relativistic theory.

Einstein's later work is comprised in what he calls the theory of general relativity. I will summarize what appear to me as the essential components of his thought, at the same time warning my readers of the danger of misrepresentation which lies in such summaries of novel ideas. It is safer to put it as my own way of envisaging the theory. What are time and space? They are the names for ways of conducting certain measurements. The four dimensions of nature as conceived by Minkowski express the fact that four measurements with a certain peculiar type of mutual independence are required to formulate the relations of any infinitesimal occurrence to the rest of the physical universe. These ways of measurement can be indefinitely varied by change of character, so that four independent measurements of one character will specify an occurrence just as well as four other measurements of some other character. A set of four measurements of a definite character which assigns a special type to each of the four measurements will be called a measure-system. Thus there are alternative measure-systems, and each measure-system embraces, for the specification of each infinitesimal occurrence, four assigned measurements of separate types, called the co-ordinates of that occurrence. The change from one measure-system to another appears in mathematics as the change from one set of variables (p_1, p_2, p_3, p_4) to another set of variables (q_1, q_2, q_3, q_4), the variables of the p-system being functions of the q-system, and *vice versa*. In this way all the quantitative laws of the physical universe can be expressed either in terms of the p-variables or in terms of the q-variables. If a suitable measure-system has been adopted, one of the measurements, say p_4, will appear to us as a measurement of time, and the remaining measurements (p_1, p_2, p_3) will be measurements of space, which are adequate to determine a point. But different measure-systems have this property of subdivision into spatial and temporal measurements according to the different circumstances of the observers. It follows that what one observer means by space and time is not necessarily the same as what another observer may mean. It is to be observed that not every change of measure-system involves a change in the meanings of space and time. For example, let (p_1, p_2, p_3, p_4) and (q_1, q_2, q_3, q_4) be the measurements in two systems which determine the same event-particle, as I will name an infinitesimal occurrence. The two measurements of time, p_4 and q_4, may be identical or may differ only by a constant; and the spatial set of the p-system, namely (p_1, p_2, p_3), may be functions of the spatial set of the q-system, namely (q_1, q_2, q_3) with q_4 excluded and *vice versa*. In this case the two systems subdivide into the same space and the same time. I will call such two systems "consentient." A measure-system which has the property for a suitable observer of thus subdividing itself I will call "spatio-temporal." I am unaware whether Einstein would accept these distinctions and definitions. If he would not I have failed to understand his theory. At the same time I would maintain them as necessary to relate the mathematical theory with the facts of physical experience.

What can we mean by space as an enduring fact, within which the varying phenomena of the universe are set at successive times? I will call space as thus con·

ceived "timeless space." All the measure-systems of a consentient spatio-temporal set will agree in specifying the same timeless space; but two spatio-temporal systems which are not consentient specify distinct timeless spaces. A point of a timeless space must be something which for all time is designated by a definite set of values for the three spatial co-ordinates of an associated measure-system. Let (p_1, p_2, p_3, p_4) be such a measure-system, then a point of the timeless p-space is to be designated by a definite specification of values for the co-ordinates in the set (p_1, p_2, p_3), giving the same entity for all values of p_4. Furthermore, according to Minkowski's conception, the life of the physical universe can be specified in terms of the intrinsic properties and mutual relations of event-particles and of aggregates of event-particles. Our problem then is narrowed down to this: how can we define the points of the timeless p-space in terms of event-particles and aggregates of event-particles? Evidently there is but one solution. The point (p_1, p_2, p_3) of the timeless p-space must be the set of event-particles indicated by giving p_4 every possible value in (p_1, p_2, p_3, p_4), while (p_1, p_2, p_3) are kept fixed to the assigned co-ordinates of the point. Two consequences follow from this definition of a point. In the first place, a point of timeless space is not an entity of any peculiar ultimate simplicity; it is a collection of event-particles.

Years ago, in a communication[2] to the Royal Society in 1906, I pointed out that the simplicity of points was inconsistent with the relational theory of space. At that time, so far as I am aware, the two inconsistent ideas were contentedly adopted by the whole of the scientific and philosophic worlds. To say that the event-particle (p_1, p_2, p_3, p_4) occupies, or happens at, the point (p_1, p_2, p_3) merely means that the event-particle is one of the set of event-particles which is the point. The second consequence of the definition is that if the p-system and the q-system are spatio-temporal systems which are not consentient, the p-points and the q-points are radically distinct entities, so that no p-point is the same as any

[2] "Mathematical Concepts of the Material World," *Phil. Trans.*

q-point. A complete explanation is thus achieved of the paradoxes in spatial measurement involved in the comparison of measurements of spatial distances between event-particles as effected in a p-space and a q-space. The ordinary formulæ which we find in the early chapters of text-books on dynamics only look so obvious because this radical distinction between the different spaces has been ignored.

We can now make a further step and distinguish between an instantaneous p-space and the one timeless p-space. Suppose that p_4 has a fixed value, then evidently every p-point is occupied by one and only one event-particle for which p_4 has this value. This event-particle has the p_1, p_2, p_3 belonging to its p-point and also the assigned value of p_4 as its four co-ordinate measurements which specify it. It is evident, therefore, that the set of event-particles which all occur at the assigned p-time p_4 but have among them all possible spatial co-ordinates together reproduce in their mutual spatial relations all the peculiarities of the relations between the points of the timeless p-space. Such a set of event-particles form the instantaneous p-space occurring at the p-time p_4. They are the instantaneous points of the instantaneous space. Also, all the instantaneous p-spaces, for different values of p_4, are correlated to each other in pointwise fashion by means of the timeless points which intersect each instantaneous space in one event-particle. An instantaneous space of some appropriate measure-system is the ideal limit of our outlook on the world when we contract our observation to be as nearly instantaneous as possible. We may conclude this part of our discussion by noting that there are three distinct meanings which may be in our mind when we talk of space, and it is mere erroneous confusion if we do not keep them apart. We may mean by space *either* (i) the unique four-dimensional manifold of event-particles *or* (ii) an assigned instantaneous space of some definite spatio-temporal measure-system, *or* (iii) the timeless space of some definite spatio-temporal measure-system.

We now turn to the consideration of time. So long as

we keep to one spatio-temporal measure-system no difficulty arises; the sets of event-particles, which are the sets of instantaneous points of successive instantaneous p-spaces ("p" being the name of the measure-system), occur in the ordered succession indicated by the successive values of p_4 (the p-time). The paradox arises when we compare the p-time p_4 with the q-time q_4 of the spatio-temporal q-system of measurement, which is not consentient with the p-system. For now if (p_1, p_2, p_3, p_4) and (q_1, q_2, q_3, q_4) indicate the same event-particle q_4 can be expressed in terms of (p_1, p_2, p_3, p_4) where p_4 and at least one of the spatial set (p_1, p_2, p_3) must occur as effective arguments to the function which expresses the value of q_4. Thus when we keep p_4 fixed, and vary (p_1, p_2, p_3) so as to run over all the event-particles of a definite instantaneous p-space, the value of q_4 alters from event-particle to event-particle. Thus two event-particles which are contemporaneous in p-time are not necessarily contemporaneous in q-time. In relation to a given event-particle E all other event-particles fall into three classes—(1) there is the class of event-particles which precede E according to the time-reckonings of all spatio-temporal measure-systems; (2) there is the class of event-particles which are contemporaneous with E in some spatio-temporal measure-system or other; (3) there is the class of event-particles which succeed E according to the time-reckonings of all spatio-temporal measure-systems. The first class is the past and the third class is the future. The second class will be called the class co-present with E. The whole class of event-particles co-present with E is not contemporaneous with E according to the time-reckoning of any one definite measure-system. Furthermore, no velocity can exist in nature, in whatever spatio-temporal measure-system it be reckoned, which could carry a material particle from one to the other of two mutually co-present event-particles. If E_1 and E_2 be a pair of mutually co-present event-particles, then E_1 precedes E_2 in some time-systems and E_2 precedes E_1 in other time-systems and E_1 and E_2 are contemporaneous in the remaining time-systems. The properties of co-present event-particles are undeniably paradoxical. We have, however, to remember that these paradoxes occur in connexion with the ultimate baffling mystery of nature—its advance from the past to the future through the medium of the present.

For any assigned observer there is yet a fourth class of event-particles—namely, that class of event-particles which comprises all nature lying within his immediate present. It must be remembered that perception is not instantaneous. Accordingly such a class is a slab of nature comprised between two instantaneous spaces belonging to the spatio-temporal measure-system which accords with the circumstances of his observation.

The physical properties of nature arise from the fact that events are not merely colourless things which happen and are gone. Each event has a character of its own. This character is analysable in two components:—(1) There are the objects situated in that event; and (2) there is the field of activity of the event which regulates the transference of the objects situated in it to situations in subsequent events. It is essential to grasp the distinction between an object and an event. An object is some entity which we can recognize, and meet again; an event passes and is gone. There are objects of radically different types, but we may confine our attention to material physical objects and to scientific objects such as electrons. Space and time have their origin in the relations between events. What we observe in nature are the situations of objects in events. Physical science analyses the fields of activity of events which determine the conditions governing the transference of objects. The whole complex of events viewed in connexion with their characters of activity takes the place of the material ether of the science of the last century. We may call it the ether of events.

Now the spatial and temporal relations of event-particles to each other are expressed by the existence in space (in whatever sense that term is used) of points, straight lines, and planes. The qualitative properties and relation of these spatial elements furnish the set conditions which are a necessary prerequisite of measurement. For it must be remembered that measurement is essentially the comparison of operations which are performed under the same set of assigned conditions. If there is no possibility of assigned conditions applicable to different circumstances, there can be no measurement. We cannot, therefore, begin to measure in space until we have determined a non-metrical geometry and have utilized it to assign the conditions of congruence agreeing with our sensible experience. Practical measurement merely requires practical conformity to definite conditions. The theoretical analysis of the practice requires the theoretical geometrical basis. For this reason I doubt the possibility of measurement in space which is heterogeneous as to its properties in different parts. I do not understand how the fixed conditions for measuerment are to be obtained. In other words, I do not see how there can be definite rules of congruence applicable under all circumstances. This objection does not touch the possibility of physical spaces of any uniform type, non-Euclidean or Euclidean. But Einstein's interpretation of his procedure postulates measurement in hererogeneous physical space, and I am very sceptical as to whether any real meaning can be attached to such a concept. I think that it must be a certain feeling for the force of this objection which has led certain men of science to explain Einstein's theory by postulating uniform space of five dimensions in which the universe is set. I cannot see how such a space, which has never entered into experience, can get over the difficulty.

There is, however, another way which obtains results identical with Einstein's to an approximation which includes all that is observable by our present methods. The only difference arises in the case of the predicted shifting of lines towards the red end of the spectrum. Here my theory makes no certain prediction. A particle vibrating in the atmosphere of the sun under an assigned harmonic force would experience an increase of apparent inertia in the ratio of 1 to $^3/_5 ga/c^2$, if vibrating radially, and in the ratio of 1 to $^2/_5 ga/c^2$, if vibrating transversely to the sun's radius, where a is the sun's radius, g is the acceleration due to gravity, and c is the critical velocity which we may roughly call the velocity of light. If we assume that the internal vibration of a molecule can be crudely represented in this fashion, and if we may assume that the internal forces of the molecule are not themselves affected in a compensatory manner by the gravitational field, then we may expect a shifting of lines towards the red end of the spectrum somewhere between three-fifths and two-fifths of Einstein's predicted amount—namely, a shift and a broadening. But both these assumptions are evidently very ill-founded. The theory does not require that any space should be other than Euclidean, and starts from the general theory of time and space which is explained in my work already cited.

I start from Einstein's great discovery that the physical field in the neighbourhood of an event-particle should be defined in terms of ten elements, which we may call by the typical name Jρσ, where ρ and σ are each written for any one of the four suffixes 1, 2, 3, 4. According to Einstein such elements merely define the properties of space and time in the neighbourhood. I interpret them as defining in Euclidean space a definite physical property of the field which I call the "impetus." I also follow Einstein in utilizing general methods of transformation from one measure-system to another, and in particular from one spatio-temporal system to another. But the essence of the divergence of the two methods lies in the fact that my law of gravitation is not expressed as the vanishing of an invariant expression, but in the more familiar way by the expression of the ten elements Jρσ in terms of two functions of which one is the ordinary gravitational potential and the other is what I call the "associate potential," which is obtained by substituting the direct distance for the inverse distance in the integral definition of the gravitational potential.